D0347688

GCSE Edexcel

Chemistry
The Workbook

This book is for anyone doing **GCSE Edexcel Chemistry**.

It's full of **tricky questions**... each one designed to make you **sweat**
— because that's the only way you'll get any **better**.

There are questions to see **what facts** you know. There are questions
to see how well you can **apply those facts**. And there are questions
to see what you know about **how science works**.

It's also got some daft bits in to try and make the whole
experience at least vaguely entertaining for you.

What CGP is all about

Our sole aim here at CGP is to produce the highest
quality books — carefully written, immaculately presented
and dangerously close to being funny.

Then we work our socks off to get them
out to you — at the cheapest possible prices.

Contents

Published by CGP

From original material by Paddy Gannon.

Editors:
Luke Antieul, Katherine Craig, Jane Sawers, Karen Wells.

Contributors:
Mike Bossart, Mike Dagless, Ian H Davis, Max Fishel, Andy Rankin,
Sidney Stringer Community School, Paul Warren, Chris Workman.

ISBN: 978 1 84762 619 6

With thanks to Barrie Crowther, Chris Elliss, Ben Fletcher, David Hickinson,
Rosie McCurrie and Hayley Thompson for the proofreading.
With thanks to Jan Greenway, Laura Jakubowski and Laura Stoney for the copyright research.

Atmospheric CO_2 graph on page 3 reproduced with kind permission from Earth System
Research Laboratory, National Oceanic and Atmospheric Administration, and Scripps Institution
of Oceanography, University of California.

Table of Use of Limestone data on pages 6 and 7 © East Midlands Aggregates Working Party
Annual Report (via National Stone Centre - publisher).

Graph of global temperature variation on page 38 reproduced with permission of the Climatic
Research Unit, School of Environmental Sciences, University of East Anglia: www.cru.uea.ac.uk.

Page 17 contains public sector information published by the Health and Safety Executive and
licensed under the Open Government Licence v1.0.

Every effort has been made to locate copyright holders and obtain permission to reproduce
sources. For those sources where it has been difficult to trace the originator of the work,
we would be grateful for information. If any copyright holder would like us to make an
amendment to the acknowledgements, please notify us and we will gladly update the book at
the next reprint. Thank you.

Groovy website: www.cgpbooks.co.uk

Printed by Elanders Ltd, Newcastle upon Tyne.
Jolly bits of clipart from CorelDRAW®
Based on the classic CGP style created by Richard Parsons.

The Evolution of the Atmosphere

Q1   Tick the boxes next to the sentences below that are **true**.

When the Earth was formed, its surface was molten. ☐

The Earth's early atmosphere is thought to have been mostly oxygen. ☐

When oxygen started building up in the atmosphere, all organisms began to thrive. ☐

When marine organisms died and were buried under layers of sediment,
the carbon inside them became locked up in carbonate rocks. ☐

Q2   The amount of **carbon dioxide** in the atmosphere has changed over the last 4.5 billion or so years.

Describe how the level of carbon dioxide has changed and explain why this change happened.

....

....

....

....

Q3   Draw lines to put the statements in the **right order** on the timeline. One is done for you.

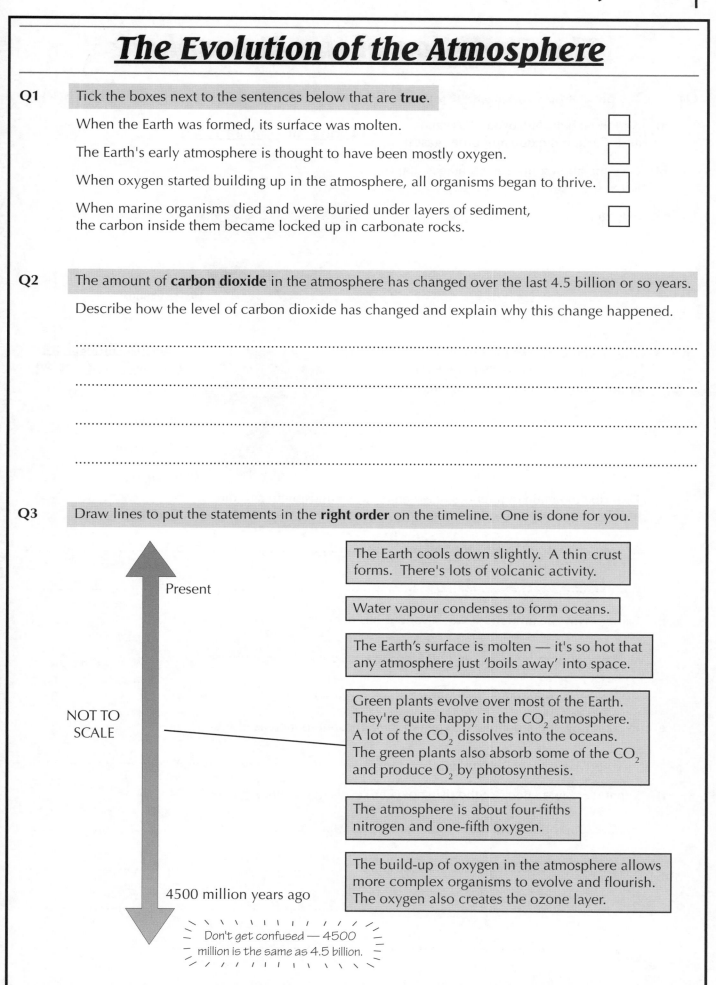

Present

NOT TO SCALE

4500 million years ago

The Earth cools down slightly. A thin crust forms. There's lots of volcanic activity.

Water vapour condenses to form oceans.

The Earth's surface is molten — it's so hot that any atmosphere just 'boils away' into space.

Green plants evolve over most of the Earth. They're quite happy in the CO_2 atmosphere. A lot of the CO_2 dissolves into the oceans. The green plants also absorb some of the CO_2 and produce O_2 by photosynthesis.

The atmosphere is about four-fifths nitrogen and one-fifth oxygen.

The build-up of oxygen in the atmosphere allows more complex organisms to evolve and flourish. The oxygen also creates the ozone layer.

Don't get confused — 4500 million is the same as 4.5 billion.

The Evolution of the Atmosphere

Q4 The pie chart below shows the proportions of the different gases in the Earth's atmosphere today.

a) Add the labels '**Nitrogen**', '**Oxygen**', and '**Carbon dioxide and other gases**'.

b) Give the approximate percentages of the following gases in the air today:

Nitrogen ....

Oxygen ....

Earth's Atmosphere Today

Water vapour

c) This pie chart shows the proportions of different gases that we think were in the Earth's atmosphere 4500 million years ago.

Earth's Atmosphere 4500 Million Years Ago

Carbon dioxide

Nitrogen

Other gases

Water vapour

Describe the main differences between today's atmosphere and the atmosphere 4500 million years ago.

....

....

d) Explain why the amount of water vapour has decreased.

....

....

What did the water vapour change into?

e) Explain how the amount of oxygen in the atmosphere increased.

....

f) What were two effects of the rising oxygen levels in the atmosphere?

1. ....

....

2. ....

....

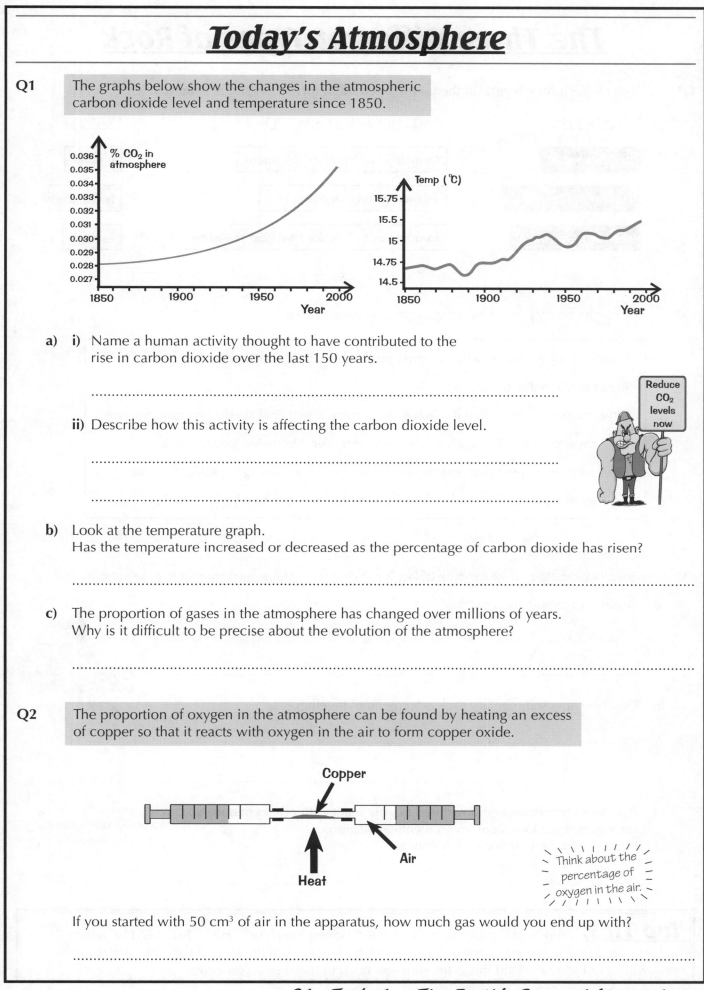

Today's Atmosphere

Q1 The graphs below show the changes in the atmospheric carbon dioxide level and temperature since 1850.

a) **i)** Name a human activity thought to have contributed to the rise in carbon dioxide over the last 150 years.

....

ii) Describe how this activity is affecting the carbon dioxide level.

....

....

b) Look at the temperature graph.
Has the temperature increased or decreased as the percentage of carbon dioxide has risen?

....

c) The proportion of gases in the atmosphere has changed over millions of years.
Why is it difficult to be precise about the evolution of the atmosphere?

....

Q2 The proportion of oxygen in the atmosphere can be found by heating an excess of copper so that it reacts with oxygen in the air to form copper oxide.

If you started with 50 cm³ of air in the apparatus, how much gas would you end up with?

....

The Three Different Types of Rock

Q1   Join up each **rock type** with the correct **method of formation** and an **example**.

ROCK TYPE   METHOD OF FORMATION   EXAMPLE

igneous rocks   formed from layers of sediment   granite

metamorphic rocks   formed when magma cools   limestone

sedimentary rocks   formed under intense heat and pressure marble

Q2   Circle the correct words to complete the passage below.

> Igneous rock is formed when magma pushes up into (or through)
>
> the **crust / mantle** and cools.
>
> If the magma cools before it reaches the surface it will **cool slowly / quickly**, forming
>
> **big / small** crystals. This rock is known as **extrusive / intrusive** igneous rock.
>
> However the magma that reaches the surface will cool **slowly / quickly**, forming
>
> **big / small** crystals. This rock is known as **extrusive / intrusive** igneous rock.

Q3   Erica notices that the stonework of her local church contains tiny fragments of **sea shells**.

a)   Suggest an explanation for this.

....

....

b)   Describe how sedimentary rock is 'cemented' together.

....

....

c)   Powdered limestone and powdered marble react with other chemicals,
such as hydrochloric acid, in an identical fashion.
Explain why the reactions are identical.

— Hint: marble is formed
from limestone.

....

Top Tips: You might think that rocks are just boring lumps of.... rock. But you'd be wrong
— rocks are actually boring lumps of different kinds of rock. And the kind of rock they are depends
on how they're formed — and this is the stuff you need to make sure you know.

The Three Different Types of Rock

Q4 The diagram below shows the formation of **metamorphic rock.**

a) Add the following labels to the diagram:

Intense heat from below

Metamorphic rock forming here

Pressure from rocks above

Possible uplift to the surface

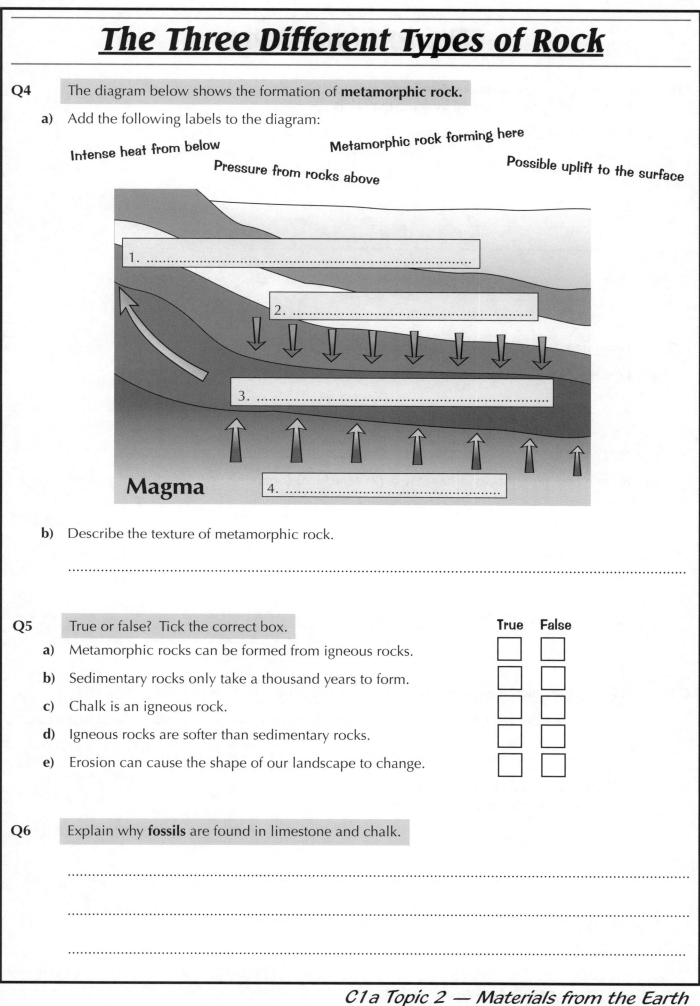

b) Describe the texture of metamorphic rock.

....

Q5 True or false? Tick the correct box.

	True	False
a) Metamorphic rocks can be formed from igneous rocks.	☐	☐
b) Sedimentary rocks only take a thousand years to form.	☐	☐
c) Chalk is an igneous rock.	☐	☐
d) Igneous rocks are softer than sedimentary rocks.	☐	☐
e) Erosion can cause the shape of our landscape to change.	☐	☐

Q6 Explain why **fossils** are found in limestone and chalk.

....

....

....

6

<u>*Using Limestone*</u>

Q1 Calcium carbonate is quarried on a large scale because it's a raw material for several **building materials**.

Name three building materials made using limestone.

1. ....

2. ....

3. ....

Q2 Limestone is a useful rock but **quarrying** it causes some **problems**.

a) Describe two problems that quarrying limestone can cause.

1. ....

2. ....

b) Explain how limestone quarries may benefit the local community.

....

....

....

Q3 In Norway **powdered limestone** is added to lakes that have been damaged by acid rain.

a) Name the process that takes place when the powdered limestone reacts with the acid in the lake.

....

b) Explain why powdered limestone is also used in the chimneys at power stations.

....

....

....

Using Limestone

Q4 This passage is about **limestone extraction** in the Peak District National Park. Read the extract and then answer the questions that follow on the next page.

The Peak District National Park covers about 1500 km² of land. Tourism is very important — a lot of people visit the area to enjoy the countryside. Limestone quarrying is also part of the local economy and there are 12 large quarries in the park. Some people aren't keen on all this — they say that quarrying is spoiling the natural beauty of the landscape, and discouraging tourists from visiting.

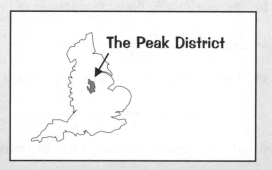
The Peak District

The limestone in the Peak District is very pure. It has been used locally in agriculture, and burned in lime kilns, for many years. When canals and railways were built in the area, limestone quarried in the park could be taken further afield, for use in industries elsewhere. This continues today, and is another cause for concern — large lorries clog up narrow roads and disturb the peace and quiet in small villages.

A lot of limestone has been dug out of the Peak District. In 2008, 7.9 million tonnes of limestone were quarried from the Peak District National Park — roughly five times as much as in 1951. This limestone is used in several different industries (the figures below are for 2008).

Use	Percentage
Aggregate (for road-building etc.)	52%
Cement	24%
Iron and steel making	2%
Chemicals and other uses	22%

Turn over the page for the questions about this article.

8

Using Limestone

a)   What makes the **limestone** from the Peak District particularly useful?

....

b)   Approximately how many tonnes of limestone were quarried in 1951?

....

c)   Describe one way in which limestone has been used locally in the Peak District.

....

d)   i)   How was limestone originally **transported away** from the Peak District?

....

ii)   How is limestone **transported** today?

....

e)   Do you think that the person who wrote the article is in favour of quarrying or against it?
Explain the reasons for your answer.

....

....

f)   Complete this table showing the amount of limestone quarried from the
Peak District in 2008.

Use	Percentage	Total amount quarried in tonnes
Aggregate (for road-building etc.)	52%	
Cement	24%	
Iron and steel making	2%	
Chemicals and other uses	22%	

C1a Topic 2 — Materials from the Earth

Limestone and Thermal Decomposition

Q1 Heating metal carbonates is an example of **thermal decomposition**.

a) Explain what **thermal decomposition** means.

....

b) **Calcium oxide** and **calcium carbonate** are both white solids.
How could you tell the difference between them?

....

c) How could you prove that carbon dioxide is produced when a metal carbonate is heated?

....

Q2 **Carbonates** decompose to form two products.

a) What is the chemical name for limestone?

....

b) Name the **two** products formed when limestone is heated.

1. ....

2. ....

c) What **solid** would be formed when **zinc carbonate** is heated?

....

d) Write a **word equation** for the reaction that occurs when **copper carbonate** is heated.

....

Q3 The hills of Northern England are dotted with the remains of **lime kilns** where **calcium carbonate** ($CaCO_3$) was heated by farmers to make **calcium oxide** (CaO).

a) Write a word equation for the reaction that takes place in a lime kiln.

....

b) Calcium oxide reacts violently with water to make calcium hydroxide ($Ca(OH)_2$).
Calcium hydroxide is a weak alkali.

What do farmers use calcium hydroxide for?

....

Limestone and Thermal Decomposition

Q4 Some carbonates thermally decompose more quickly than others.

a) You can carry out an experiment to find how easily some carbonates thermally decompose. Number the boxes 1 to 5 to put the method in order.

☐ **Repeat for each carbonate.**

☐ **Compare your results.**

☐ **Pipe off the gas into a test tube of limewater.**

☐ **Heat the carbonate in a boiling tube.**

☐ **Record the time taken for the limewater to change colour.**

b) Draw the **apparatus** used for this experiment in the box below.

c) i) How would you know which carbonate had decomposed the **fastest**?

....

ii) Why do carbonates decompose at **different** speeds?

....

d) Apart from the change in the limewater, what else might you notice when a carbonate thermally decomposes?

....

Atoms and Mass in Chemical Reactions

Q1 Use the words below to fill the gaps in the passage.
You might need to use some words more than once.

constant	atoms	rearranged	mass	particles

Elements and compounds are made up of .... and these are the

smallest .... you can get of each element.

It's the .... that take part in chemical reactions. During reactions they

aren't lost or made, they are just .... Because of this the

.... at the start and end of a reaction remains ....

Q2 When copper sulfate and sodium hydroxide react a **precipitate** forms.

a) What is a precipitate?

....

b) The precipitate formed is copper hydroxide. Write a **word equation** for this reaction.

....

c) If you started with 12 g of copper sulfate and 15 g of sodium hydroxide,
what would the total mass of the products be?

....

....

Q3 18 g of calcium oxide were reacted with some water.

a) The mass of the product at the end of the reaction was 29 g.
What mass of water was used?

....

....

b) Would you expect the properties of the product to be different from
the properties of the reactants?

....

Balancing Equations

Q1   Tick the boxes to show which of the following equations are **balanced** correctly.

		Correctly balanced	Incorrectly balanced
a)	$H_2 + Cl_2 \rightarrow 2HCl$	☐	☐
b)	$CuO + HCl \rightarrow CuCl_2 + H_2O$	☐	☐
c)	$N_2 + H_2 \rightarrow NH_3$	☐	☐
d)	$CuO + H_2 \rightarrow Cu + H_2O$	☐	☐
e)	$CaCO_3 \rightarrow CaO + CO_2$	☐	☐

Q2   Here is the equation for the formation of carbon **mon**oxide in a poorly ventilated gas fire. It is **not** balanced correctly.

$$C + O_2 \rightarrow CO$$

Circle the **correctly balanced** version of this equation.

$$C + O_2 \rightarrow CO_2$$

$$C + O_2 \rightarrow 2CO$$

$$2C + O_2 \rightarrow 2CO$$

Q3   In a book, this is the description of a reaction: "**methane** (CH_4) can be burnt in **oxygen** (O_2) to make **carbon dioxide** (CO_2) and **water** (H_2O)".

a) What are the **reactants** and the **products** in this reaction?

Reactants: ....   Products: ....

b) Write the **word equation** for this reaction.

....

c) Write the **balanced symbol equation** for the reaction.

Don't forget the oxygen ends up in both products

....

Top Tips: The most important thing to remember with balancing equations is that you can't change the **little numbers** — if you do that then you'll change the substance into something completely different. Just take your time and work through everything logically.

Balancing Equations

Q4   Write out the balanced **symbol** equations for the unbalanced picture equations below.

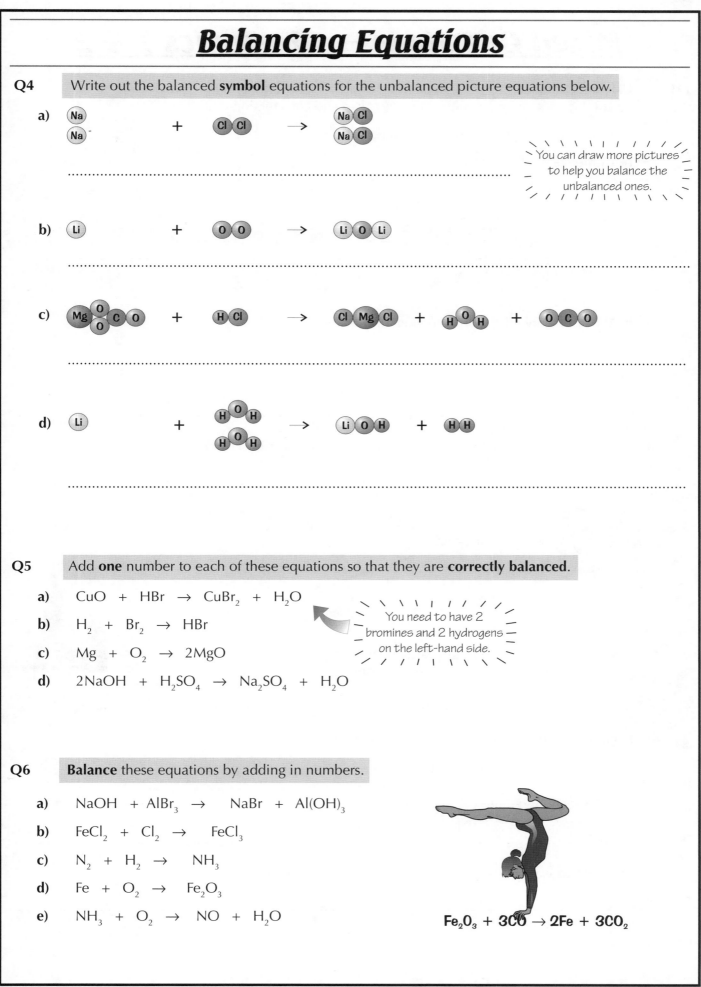

a)

You can draw more pictures to help you balance the unbalanced ones.

....

b)

....

c)

....

d)

....

Q5   Add **one** number to each of these equations so that they are **correctly balanced**.

a) $CuO + HBr \rightarrow CuBr_2 + H_2O$

b) $H_2 + Br_2 \rightarrow HBr$

c) $Mg + O_2 \rightarrow 2MgO$

d) $2NaOH + H_2SO_4 \rightarrow Na_2SO_4 + H_2O$

You need to have 2 bromines and 2 hydrogens on the left-hand side.

Q6   **Balance** these equations by adding in numbers.

a) $NaOH + AlBr_3 \rightarrow NaBr + Al(OH)_3$

b) $FeCl_2 + Cl_2 \rightarrow FeCl_3$

c) $N_2 + H_2 \rightarrow NH_3$

d) $Fe + O_2 \rightarrow Fe_2O_3$

e) $NH_3 + O_2 \rightarrow NO + H_2O$

$Fe_2O_3 + 3CO \rightarrow 2Fe + 3CO_2$

C1a Topic 2 — Materials from the Earth

Mixed Questions — C1a Topics 1 & 2

Q1 **Calcium carbonate** ($CaCO_3$), in the form of the rock **limestone**, is one of the most important raw materials for the chemical and construction industries.

a) Limestone can be processed to form **limewater**.

i) Complete the flow diagram.

common name	limestone		limewater
chemical name	calcium carbonate		
formula	$CaCO_3$	CaO	

+ HEAT (REACTION A) → + WATER (REACTION B) →

ii) Write a balanced symbol equation for reaction A.

.... → .... + ...

iii) Give one use of limewater.

....

b) Limestone can be processed to form useful building materials. Complete the flow diagram.

Limestone

heat with clay →

add sand, water and gravel →

heat with sand and sodium carbonate →

c) The limestone of the Houses of Parliament is crumbling away. What is causing the damage to the limestone and how?

....

d) Limestone is turned into **marble** by a natural process.

i) Describe this process.

....

....

ii) Give two ways in which marble is different from limestone.

1. ....

2. ....

Mixed Questions — C1a Topics 1 & 2

Q2 The graphs below give information about the Earth's atmosphere millions of years ago and today.

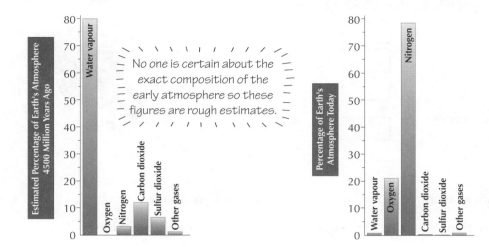

No one is certain about the exact composition of the early atmosphere so these figures are rough estimates.

a) Could the early atmosphere **support life** as we know it? Explain your answer.

....

....

b) Which **organisms** caused an increase in oxygen and a decrease in carbon dioxide?

....

c) Even though the level of **carbon dioxide** is much lower now than millions of years ago, in the last 250 years the level has **increased**. Complete the following passage by circling the correct words.

> Humans are **increasing** / **decreasing** the amount of **carbon dioxide** / **oxygen** in the atmosphere by **burning** / **creating** fossil fuels. Also, deforestation **reduces** / **increases** the amount of carbon dioxide **absorbed** / **released** from the atmosphere.

d) Tick the correct boxes to indicate whether each statement is **true** or **false**.

	True	False
i) About 10% of the present atmosphere is noble gases, such as argon.	☐	☐
ii) Very early in Earth's history volcanoes gave out gases.	☐	☐
iii) Green plants take in oxygen and give out carbon dioxide during photosynthesis.	☐	☐

e) Why is it difficult to be precise about the evolution of the atmosphere?

....

....

Mixed Questions — C1a Topics 1 & 2

Q3   State symbols give the **physical state** of a substance.

Give the **symbols** for the following states.

a) Solid ☐

b) Liquid ☐

c) Gas ☐

d) Dissolved in water
(aqueous) ☐

Q4   Change these **word equations** into balanced **symbol equations**.

a) **Word equation:**   zinc carbonate → zinc oxide + carbon dioxide

Symbol equation: ....

b) **Word equation:**   copper + oxygen → copper oxide

Symbol equation: ....

c) **Word equation:**   calcium oxide + water → calcium hydroxide

Symbol equation: ....

Q5   Bob thinks that the total mass in a reaction remains **constant**.

a) Describe an experiment using a precipitation reaction that he could do to prove this.

....

....

....

b) If he tried to prove that the total mass in a reaction remains constant using a thermal decomposition reaction of a carbonate, why would it be important to use sealed apparatus?

....

....

c) Explain why the mass of reactants always equals the mass of the products.

....

Hazard Symbols

Q1   True or false? Put a tick in the correct box.

		True	False
a)	Hazard symbols are found on the packaging of all chemicals.	☐	☐
b)	Hazard symbols show you what the dangers associated with a chemical are.	☐	☐
c)	All chemicals are toxic.	☐	☐
d)	Hazard symbols help you to choose safe-working procedures in the lab.	☐	☐
e)	You shouldn't use chemicals with more than three hazard symbols on the packaging.	☐	☐
f)	Hazard symbols are only found on chemicals that are extremely dangerous.	☐	☐
g)	You should always look at the hazard symbols for a chemical before using it.	☐	☐

Q2   Draw lines to match the **symbols** below with their **meanings** and **hazards**.

a)   toxic   can cause death if swallowed, inhaled or absorbed through the skin

b)   corrosive   causes reddening or blistering of the skin

c)   highly flammable   provides oxygen which allows other materials to burn more fiercely

d)   irritant   attacks and destroys living tissue

e)   harmful   like toxic, but not quite as dangerous

f)   oxidising   catches fire easily

Acids and Alkalis

Q1 Complete the following sentences about **acids** and **alkalis**.

a) Solutions which are not alkaline or neutral are said to be ....

b) A substance with a pH less than 7 is called an ....

c) A substance with a pH more than 7 is called a ....

d) An alkali is a base that dissolves in ....

e) The pH of pure water is ....

Q2 Draw lines to match **universal indicator colour** to **pH** value and **acid/alkali strength**.

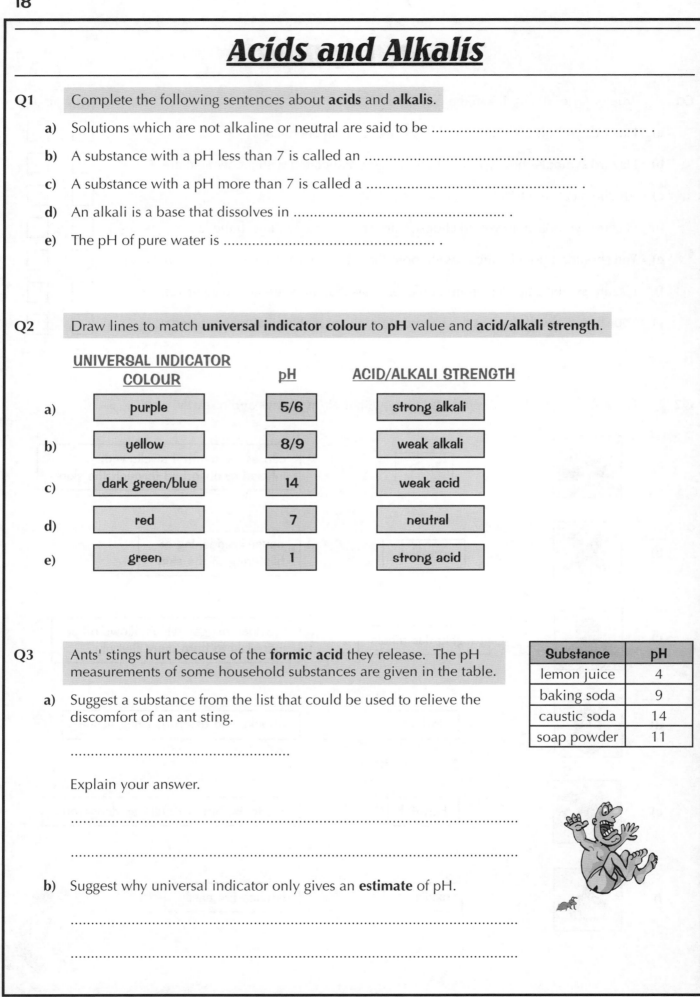

	UNIVERSAL INDICATOR COLOUR	pH	ACID/ALKALI STRENGTH
a)	purple	5/6	strong alkali
b)	yellow	8/9	weak alkali
c)	dark green/blue	14	weak acid
d)	red	7	neutral
e)	green	1	strong acid

Q3 Ants' stings hurt because of the **formic acid** they release. The pH measurements of some household substances are given in the table.

Substance	pH
lemon juice	4
baking soda	9
caustic soda	14
soap powder	11

a) Suggest a substance from the list that could be used to relieve the discomfort of an ant sting.

....

Explain your answer.

....

....

b) Suggest why universal indicator only gives an **estimate** of pH.

....

....

Hydrochloric Acid and Indigestion Tablets

Q1   Fill in the blanks using the words below.

base	indigestion	acidic	digestion	too much
neutralise	too little	alkaline	kill	

The stomach produces hydrochloric acid to help with .... The enzymes

which break down food in the stomach work best in an .... environment.

Having acid in the stomach also helps to .... bacteria — making it less

likely that you'll go down with some kind of nasty food poisoning. Indigestion is caused by

.... hydrochloric acid in the stomach. Indigestion tablets contain a

.... such as calcium carbonate, which will .... the acid.

Q2   **Antacid tablets** contain **alkalis** to neutralise the excess stomach acid that causes indigestion.

Joey wanted to test how well different antacid tablets neutralise acid. He dissolved each type
of tablet in distilled water and added a few drops of indicator. Joey put hydrochloric acid in a
burette and added it to the antacid tablet solution until it had been neutralised. He then read
off how much acid was left in the burette. His results for five different tablets are shown in the
table below.

Tablet	Volume of HCl at start of experiment / cm³	Volume of HCl left at end of experiment / cm³	Volume of HCl needed to neutralise tablet / cm³
A	50.0	35.2	14.8
B	46.9	31.0	
C	37.5	14.1	
D	49.3	32.6	
E	42.2	35.6	

a)   Complete the table to show the amount of acid required to neutralise each tablet.
The first one has been done for you.

b)   Which tablet requires the smallest amount of acid to neutralise it?

....

c)   One of the antacids requires you to take **two** tablets as a **single dose**. The others require
you to take just one. Which of the antacids, A to E, do you think requires two tablets?

....

d)   Which tablet is most effective in a **single dose**? Explain your answer.

....

....

Reactions of Acids

Q1 Give the **general word equation** for the reaction between an **acid** and a **metal hydroxide**.

....

Q2 Give the **general word equation** for the reaction between an **acid** and a **metal oxide**.

....

Q3 Fill in the blanks to complete the word equations for **acids** reacting with **metal oxides** and **metal hydroxides**.

a) hydrochloric acid + lead oxide → .... chloride + water

b) nitric acid + copper hydroxide → copper .... + water

c) sulfuric acid + zinc oxide → zinc sulfate + ...

d) hydrochloric acid + ... oxide → nickel .... + ...

e) .... acid + copper oxide → .... nitrate + ...

f) sulfuric acid + ... hydroxide →

   sodium .... + ...

g) hydrochloric acid + ... hydroxide →

   calcium .... + ...

Reactions of Acids

Q4 **Complete** the following equations.

a) $H_2SO_{4(aq)}$ + ... → $CuSO_{4(aq)}$ + $H_2O_{(l)}$

b) $2HNO_{3(aq)}$ + $MgO_{(s)}$ → $Mg(NO_3)_{2(aq)}$ + ...

c) .... + $KOH_{(aq)}$ → $KCl_{(aq)}$ + $H_2O_{(l)}$

d) $2HCl_{(aq)}$ + ... → $ZnCl_{2(aq)}$ + $H_2O_{(l)}$

e) $H_2SO_{4(aq)}$ + $2NaOH_{(aq)}$ → .... + ...

f) $HNO_{3(aq)}$ + $KOH_{(s)}$ → .... + ...

g) .... + $ZnO_{(s)}$ → $ZnSO_{4(aq)}$ + ...

Q5 **Balance** the following acid/base reactions.

a) H_3PO_4 + $NaOH$ → Na_3PO_4 + H_2O

b) $NaOH$ + H_2SO_4 → Na_2SO_4 + H_2O

c) $Mg(OH)_2$ + HNO_3 → $Mg(NO_3)_2$ + H_2O

d) NH_3 + H_2SO_4 → $(NH_4)_2SO_4$

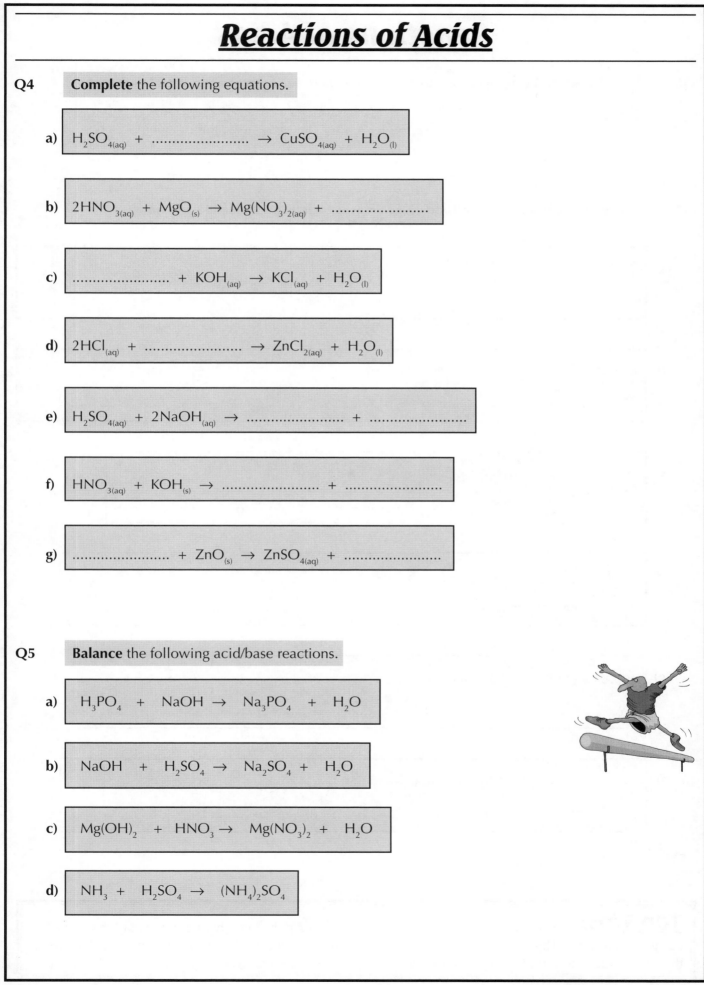

Reactions of Acids

Q6 Give the **general word equation** for the reaction between an **acid** and a **metal carbonate**.

....

Q7 Complete the following word equations for **acids** reacting with **metal carbonates**.

a) Nitric acid + sodium carbonate →

.... + ... + ...

b) Calcium carbonate + hydrochloric acid →

.... + ... + ...

c) .... + sulfuric acid →

zinc sulfate + ... + ...

d) Nitric acid + ... →

magnesium nitrate + ... + ...

e) Copper carbonate + ... →

copper chloride + ... + ...

f) .... + ... →

magnesium sulfate + ... + ...

Top Tips: Take your time over these — it's easy to zip through them and misread the names of the compounds. Think logically — you can't have any elements in the products that weren't there at the start of the reaction. If you get stuck check back over the general word equation.

Reactions of Acids

Q8   Fill in the blanks in the following statements about **metal** and **acid** reactions.

a)   Hydrochloric acid always gives .... salts.

b)   Nitric acid always gives .... salts.

c)   Sulfuric acid always gives .... salts.

Q9   **Complete** the following symbol equations. Remember to include state symbols.

a) $H_2SO_{4(aq)}$ + ... → $CuSO_{4(aq)}$ + $H_2O_{(l)}$ + $CO_{2(g)}$

b) $2HNO_{3(aq)}$ + ... → $Mg(NO_3)_{2(aq)}$ + H_2O + ...

c) $2HCl_{(aq)}$ + ... → $ZnCl_{2(aq)}$ + $H_2O_{(l)}$ + $CO_{2(g)}$

d) $H_2SO_{4(aq)}$ + $Na_2CO_{3(aq)}$ → .... + ... + ...

Q10   **Balance** the following acid/base reactions.

a) HCl + $CaCO_3$ → $CaCl_2$ + H_2O + CO_2

b) HCl + K_2CO_3 → KCl + H_2O + CO_2

c) HNO_3 + $ZnCO_3$ → $Zn(NO_3)_2$ + H_2O + CO_2

d) Na_2CO_3 + HCl → $NaCl$ + H_2O + CO_2

Electrolysis

Q1 Fill in the blanks in the passage below using the words provided.

electrical energy	direct current	gas
	electrodes	electrolyte

Electrolysis is the breaking down (decomposition) of a compound using

.... The electricity used comes from a ....

source, such as a battery. It requires a liquid to conduct the electricity, called

an .... The electricity is applied to the liquid by two

.... The electrolyte contains the compound, which is broken

down into its component parts. The component parts are released as atoms or molecules

— often as a ....

Q2 Electrolysis of dilute **hydrochloric acid** gives **two** gases.

a) Name the two gases produced.

Gas 1: .... Gas 2: ....

b) Describe a simple **laboratory test** you would use to identify each of the gases.

Test for gas 1 ....

....

Test for gas 2 ....

....

Q3 After electrolysing a salt solution, Englebert noticed that the laboratory had a similar smell to his local **swimming pool**.

Think about the uses of chlorine.

a) Suggest why this was. ....

....

b) Explain why this could be a safety issue.

....

c) Suggest what could be done in future to make this experiment safer.

....

Electrolysis

Q4 Harry runs a little **sea water electrolysis** business from his garden shed. He keeps a record of all the different **industries** that he sells his products to.

HARRY'S SEA WATER PRODUCTS LTD.
— FINAL USES

disinfectants 11%
other 20%
margarine x%
plastics 33%
other 5%
insecticide 6%

chlorine
hydrogen

a) Which sea water product does Harry sell the most of?

....

b) What percentage of Harry's products are used to manufacture **margarine**?

....

c) Which **industry** uses the biggest proportion of Harry's products?

....

Q5 Sammy decides to carry out the electrolysis of **water** in his bedroom.

a) Name the two gases produced by the electrolysis of water.

....

b) Sammy's mother is worried that he's doing a dangerous experiment using concentrated hydrochloric acid. Sammy says that he can prove her wrong by testing the gases given off. Explain what he would do and what it would show.

....

....

....

....

....

....

Metal Ores

Q1 Indicate whether each of the statements below about **metal ores** is true or false.

True False

a) Metal ores are found in the Earth's crust. ☐ ☐

b) Ores are metal compounds that contain enough metal to make extraction worthwhile. ☐ ☐

c) The more reactive the metal, the easier it is to extract from its ore. ☐ ☐

d) Zinc and iron can both be extracted by heating their ores with carbon. ☐ ☐

Q2 Copper may have been formed when someone accidentally dropped some copper ore into a **wood fire**. When the ashes were cleared away some copper was left.

Explain how dropping the ore into the fire led to the extraction of copper.

....

....

Remember that wood contains carbon.

Q3 Fill in the blanks in the passage below.

.... can be used to extract metals that are

.... it in the reactivity series. Oxygen is removed

from the metal oxide in a process called ....

Other metals have to be extracted using .... because

they are .... reactive.

Q4 Some metals are found as **ores**. Others, such as gold, are usually found as **elements**.

a) Explain why gold is usually found as an element.

....

b) i) One type of iron ore is magnetite (Fe_3O_4).
Write a balanced symbol equation for its formation from iron (Fe) and oxygen (O_2).

....

ii) Is the iron **oxidised** or **reduced** in this reaction? ....

c) i) Write a balanced symbol equation to show the reaction that happens when copper is extracted from its ore, CuO, using carbon.

....

ii) Is the copper **oxidised** or **reduced** in this reaction? ....

Reduction of Metal Ores

Q1 Some metals can be **extracted** by heating their ore with **carbon**.

a) Explain why **iron** can be extracted from iron oxide by heating with **carbon**.

....

b) Write the **word equation** for the reduction of iron oxide with carbon.

....

c) **Complete** and **balance** the symbol equation for this reaction.

......Fe_2O_3 + ... → .... + ...

d) Not all metals can be extracted using this method.
Tick the boxes below to show which metals **cannot** be extracted this way.

Potassium ☐

Magnesium ☐

Tin ☐

Calcium ☐

Aluminium ☐

Sodium ☐

Lead ☐

Q2 Read the following passage about **zinc** extraction then answer the questions below.

> Zinc is most commonly found as the ore sphalerite (mainly zinc sulfide, ZnS).
> The sphalerite is first processed to remove impurities such as iron, copper and lead sulfides.
> Then it is converted to zinc oxide and sulfur dioxide by heating it with air.
> Finally, the zinc oxide is reduced by heating it to 950 °C with carbon.

a) What is the **name** and **chemical formula** of the most common zinc ore?

Name ....   Chemical formula ....

b) Write a **word equation** for the conversion of this ore to zinc oxide.

....

c) Give the balanced **symbol equation** for the reaction of **zinc oxide** with carbon.

....

Reduction of Metal Ores

Q3 Draw lines to join these words with their correct meanings.

Electrolysis

Used to apply electricity to the liquid.

Electrolyte

The breakdown of a substance using electricity.

Electrode

The liquid that is used in electrolysis.

Q4 Are these statements about the extraction of **aluminium** true or false?

True   False

a) Substances can only be electrolysed if they're molten or in solution. ☐ ☐

b) Aluminium is extracted from its ore, bauxite. ☐ ☐

c) Hydrogen gas is given off during the extraction of aluminium by electrolysis. ☐ ☐

d) Aluminium is collected at the electrodes. ☐ ☐

e) Aluminium has to be extracted by electrolysis because it's lower than carbon in the reactivity series. ☐ ☐

Q5 The diagram below shows the electrolysis of **aluminium oxide**.

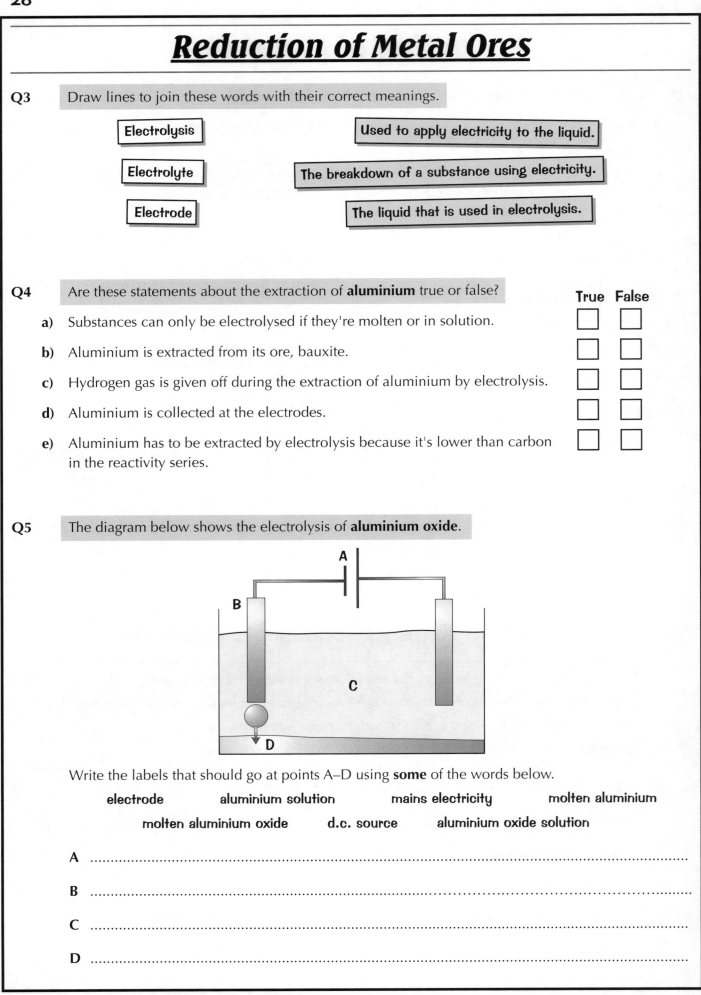

Write the labels that should go at points A–D using **some** of the words below.

electrode   aluminium solution   mains electricity   molten aluminium

molten aluminium oxide   d.c. source   aluminium oxide solution

A ....

B ....

C ....

D ....

Properties of Metals

Q1   This table shows some of the **properties** of four different **metals**.

Metal	Heat conduction	Cost	Resistance to corrosion	Strength
1	average	high	excellent	good
2	average	medium	good	excellent
3	excellent	low	good	good
4	low	high	average	poor

Use the information in the table to choose which metal would be **best** for making each of the following:

a)   Saucepan bases ....

b)   Car bodies ....

c)   A statue to be placed in a town centre ....

Think about how long a statue would have to last for.

Q2   What **properties** would you look for if you were asked to choose a **metal** suitable for making knives and forks?

....

....

....

Q3   For each of the following **applications** of metals, say which **property** of the metal makes it ideal for the given use. Choose the best answer from the list of typical properties of metals below. You may only use each property **once**.

ductile   low density   resists corrosion   conducts heat

a)   Aluminium is used to make aircraft.   ....

b)   Copper is used to make the base of saucepans and frying pans.   ....

c)   Gold is used by dentists to make long-lasting fillings and false teeth. ....

d)   Copper is drawn out into thin wires for electrical cables.   ....

Top Tips: Remember most elements are metals and most metals have similar properties. But don't be a fool and think they're all identical — there are lots of little differences which make them useful for different things. Some metals are pretty weird, for example mercury is liquid at room temperature, which means it's not ideal for making cars.

Properties of Metals

Q4 In an experiment some identically sized rods of different materials (A, B, C and D) were **heated** at one end and **temperature sensors** were connected to the other ends. The results are shown in the graph.

a) Which two rods do you think were made from metals?

....

b) Which of the metals was the best conductor of heat and how can you tell?

....

Q5 Imagine that a space probe has brought a sample of a new element back from Mars. Scientists think that the element is a **metal**, but they aren't certain. Give **three properties** they could look for to provide evidence that the element is a **metal**.

1. ....

2. ....

3. ....

Q6 Use some of the words below to **complete** this passage about corrosion. You can only use each word once.

all	less	dissolved	slowly	oxidised
more	easily	some	reduced	

Over time, ... metals corrode. Corrosion happens because

the metal is being .... Metals which are high in the reactivity

series are .... likely to corrode because they react more

.... with oxygen. For example, iron is ....

corrosion-resistant than lead.

Making Metals More Useful

Q1 Most iron is made into the alloy **steel**.

a) Write a definition of the term '**alloy**'.

....

....

b) How is **iron** turned into **steel**?

....

....

Tonight Matthew, I'm going to be... steel.

Q2 Draw lines to connect the correct phrases in each column. One has been done for you.

Metal / Alloy	What has been added	Use
low-carbon steel	nothing	blades for tools
iron from a blast furnace	chromium	cutlery
high-carbon steel	0.1% carbon	car bodies
stainless steel	1.5% carbon	ornamental railings

Q3 Complete the following sentences using some of the metals below.

gold   copper   platinum   titanium   nickel   iron   zinc

a) Nitinol is an alloy that contains .... and ....

b) To make gold hard enough for jewellery it is mixed with metals such as

.... , ... and ....

c) Gold alloys are measured in carats, which indicates the proportion of pure ....

<u>*Making Metals More Useful*</u>

Q4   24-carat gold is **pure** gold. 9-carat gold contains **9 parts** gold to 15 parts other metals.
9-carat gold is **harder** and **cheaper** than 24-carat gold.

   a)   What percentage of 9-carat gold is actually gold?

   ....

   b)   Why is 9-carat gold harder than pure gold?

   ....

   ....

Q5   Gold alloys can be described by **carats** or **fineness**.

   a)   Explain what 'fineness' means.

   ....

   b)   Use lines to link the correct parts of the following sentences.

   900 fineness is the same as   **1 carat gold.**

   042 fineness is the same as   **a gold alloy with 25% other metals.**

   375 fineness is the same as   **9 carat gold.**

   750 fineness is the same as   **90% pure gold.**

Q6   Recently, scientists have been developing **smart alloys**.

   a)   Give an example of a use for smart alloys.

   ....

   b) **i)**   Name **one** property which some smart alloys have
         that normal alloys don't.

   Smart Alloy of the
   Month Award
   Presented to: <u>Nitinol</u>
   Presented by: <u>CGP</u>

   ....

   ii)   What **advantage** does this give smart alloys?

   ....

   ....

<u>*Top Tips:*</u>   As you must know by now, metals have lots of pretty useful properties, but they can
be made even more useful by being mixed together to make alloys. However, it's possible to go one
step further and make smart alloys. The clue's in the name — they're like normal alloys, but smarter.

Recycling

Q1 Give **three** advantages of **recycling metals**.

1. ....

2. ....

3. ....

Q2 Tick the correct boxes to show whether the following statements are **true** or **false**.

		True	False
a)	Recycling could help to prevent further increases in greenhouse gas levels.	☐	☐
b)	It is important to recycle copper because there is a finite amount available.	☐	☐
c)	Recycling costs nothing and has huge benefits for the environment.	☐	☐

Q3 Below is some information about **aluminium**, a widely used metal today.

> Bauxite (aluminium ore) gives 1 kg of aluminium for every 4 kg of bauxite mined.
>
> Bauxite mines are often located in rainforests.
>
> Extracting aluminium from bauxite requires huge quantities of electricity.
>
> An aluminium can weighs about 20 g.

a) **i)** How much ore has to be mined to produce 1 tonne (1000 kg) of aluminium?

....

ii) Australians used about 3 billion aluminium cans in 2002.
How many tonnes of aluminium does this represent?

....

iii) How many tonnes of bauxite were mined to supply Australians with aluminium cans in 2002?

....

b) Outline the **environmental** consequences of:

i) Mining the bauxite. ....

....

ii) Extracting the aluminium. ....

....

iii) Not recycling the cans. ....

....

Fractional Distillation of Crude Oil

Q1 Circle the correct words to complete these sentences.

a) Crude oil is a **mixture** / **compound** of different molecules.

b) Crude oil contains **carbohydrate** / **hydrocarbon** molecules.

c) The molecules in crude oil **are** / **aren't** chemically bonded to each other.

d) Physical methods **can** / **can't** be used to separate out the molecules in crude oil.

Q2 Name the two elements that **hydrocarbons** are made up of.

....

Q3 The molecules listed below are in order of **smallest** to **largest** from left to right.
Label this diagram of a **fractionating column** to show where these substances can be collected.

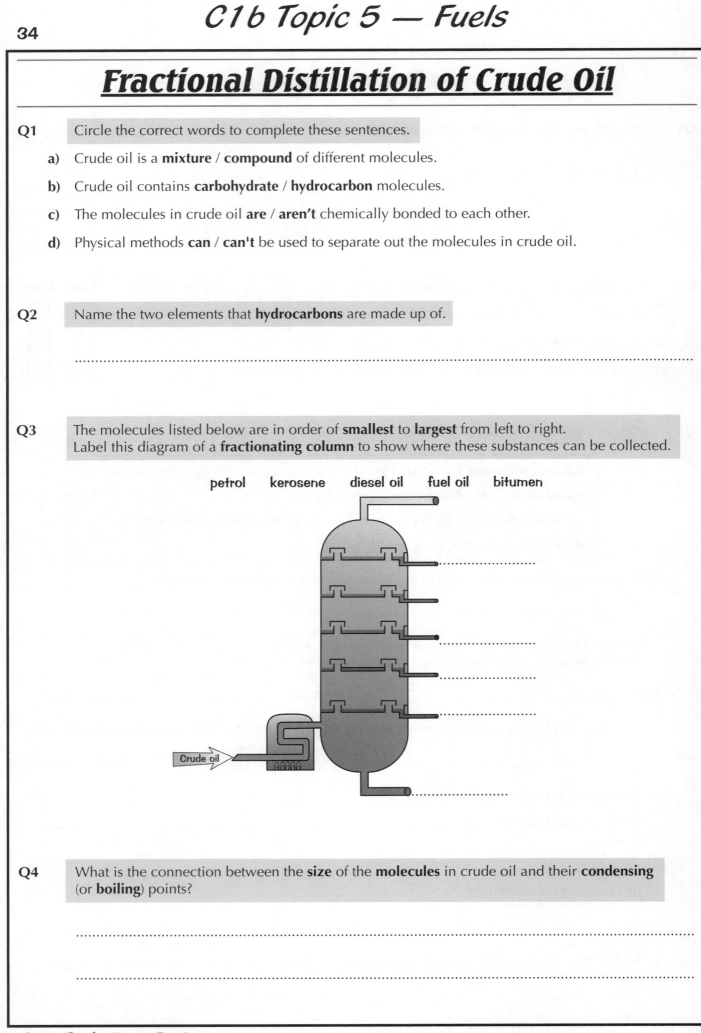

petrol   kerosene   diesel oil   fuel oil   bitumen

Crude oil

Q4 What is the connection between the **size** of the **molecules** in crude oil and their **condensing** (or **boiling**) points?

....

....

Fractional Distillation of Crude Oil

Q5   Draw lines to match up each crude oil **fraction** to its most common use.

Gas   Used to surface roads and roofs

Petrol   Used as a fuel for lorries, trains and some cars

Kerosene   Used as an aircraft fuel

Diesel Oil   Used for cooking and heating

Fuel Oil   Used as a fuel for cars

Bitumen   Used as a fuel for ships and some power stations

phwoar... nice tank, love

Q6   Use some of the words below to fill the gaps in the passage.

viscous	chlorine	carbon	lower	ignite	hydrogen	higher

Fractions that are tapped off at the top of the fractionating column have

.... boiling points than fractions tapped off at the bottom.

They also have fewer .... and .... atoms.

The shorter the molecules in the fraction, the more easily they ....

Also the shorter the molecules the less .... they are.

Q7   Petrol is a **non-renewable** fossil fuel.

Explain why petrol is **non-renewable**.

....

....

....

Top Tips: So many of the things around us that we take for granted are made from the products of crude oil. It's a bit of a pain really 'cos that's why the examiner thinks it's important. Remember that the length of a hydrocarbon molecule affects its boiling point and how flammable it is. Oh, and for extra marks, don't forget to learn the uses of all those lovely fractions too.

Burning Fuels

Q1　Answer the following questions about **burning hydrocarbons**.

a)　Write a **word equation** for the complete combustion of a hydrocarbon.

....

b)　Circle the correct words from each pair in the sentences below.

> When a hydrocarbon is burnt, the carbon and hydrogen are **oxidised / reduced.**
>
> The reaction **gives out / takes in** energy

Q2　When choosing fuels there are a number of **factors** which must be taken into consideration. Give three factors that are important when choosing a fuel to be used in a car engine.

1. ....

2. ....

3. ....

Q3　Answer the following questions about **hydrocarbons**.

a)　Underline the two correct formulae for the products of the complete combustion of a hydrocarbon.

H_2S　　　　CH_4　　　　CO_2　　　　SO_2　　　　H_2O

b)　Suggest why a fuel might not burn completely.

....

....

Q4　**Incomplete combustion** can cause problems.

a)　Fill in the blanks to complete the word equation for the incomplete combustion of hydrocarbons.

hydrocarbon + oxygen → .... + ...

+ .... + ...

b)　Why is it dangerous if incomplete combustion occurs in household gas appliances?

....

....

Environmental Problems

Q1   Explain why **sulfur dioxide** is produced when some hydrocarbons are burnt.

....

....

Q2   Draw lines to link the correct parts of these sentences.

| The main cause of acid rain is | acid rain. |

The main cause of acid rain is

Acid rain kills trees and

Limestone buildings and statues are affected by

In clouds sulfur dioxide reacts with water to make

acid rain.

sulfuric acid.

acidifies lakes.

sulfur dioxide.

Q3   Give **three** ways that the amount of **acid rain** can be reduced.

1. ....

2. ....

3. ....

Q4   Scientists are working hard to develop **new technologies** that are environmentally friendly.

Do you think it is solely the responsibility of scientists to find ways of reducing environmental damage or should people be prepared to change their lifestyles too? Explain your answer.

....

....

....

There's no right or wrong answer here — the key is being able to explain your reasoning.

Top Tips: Don't panic, acid rain won't burn your skin off. That said, it's not your average harmless old drizzle either — it has far reaching effects, as the pollutants that cause it can get carried a long way. Plus, there are soot particles, carbon monoxide and carbon dioxide to think about as well. All in all, burning hydrocarbons is a dirty business and we'll need to clean up our act sooner or later.

More Environmental Problems

Q1 Underline the statements below about the greenhouse effect that are **true**.

- The greenhouse effect is needed for life on Earth as we know it.

- Greenhouse gases include carbon dioxide and methane.

- Human activity isn't affecting the amount of greenhouse gases.

- Increasing amounts of greenhouse gases are causing global warming.

Q2 The graph shows the average temperature of the Earth between **1961** and **1990**, and how the temperature has differed from it over the last **150 years**.

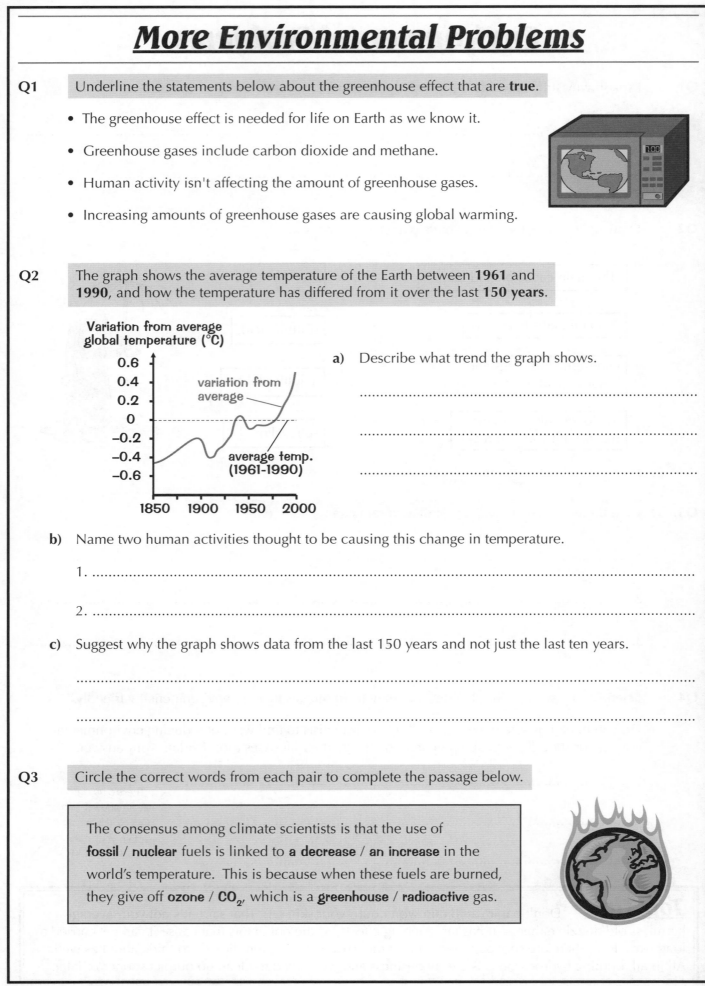

Variation from average global temperature (°C)

variation from average

average temp. (1961-1990)

0.6 0.4 0.2 0 −0.2 −0.4 −0.6

1850 1900 1950 2000

a) Describe what trend the graph shows.

....

....

....

b) Name two human activities thought to be causing this change in temperature.

1. ....

2. ....

c) Suggest why the graph shows data from the last 150 years and not just the last ten years.

....

....

Q3 Circle the correct words from each pair to complete the passage below.

The consensus among climate scientists is that the use of **fossil / nuclear** fuels is linked to **a decrease / an increase** in the world's temperature. This is because when these fuels are burned, they give off **ozone / CO_2**, which is a **greenhouse / radioactive** gas.

More Environmental Problems

Q4 **Carbon dioxide** and **methane** are two atmospheric gases which are important in the regulation of the Earth's **temperature**.

a) Which of A, B, C and D best explains how CO_2 and methane help regulate the Earth's temperature? Circle your answer.

A They absorb heat from the Sun.   B They keep the polar ice caps from melting.

C They absorb heat from the Earth.   D They counteract acid rain.

b) Explain how you add to carbon dioxide production if:

i) you are driven to school in a car instead of walking.

....

ii) you leave the TV on standby all night.

....

Q5 Tick the boxes to show whether the following statements are **true** or **false**.

		True	False
a)	Oxygen is released when trees are burnt to clear the land.	☐	☐
b)	Living trees remove CO_2 from the atmosphere during photosynthesis.	☐	☐
c)	Chopping down trees helps to reduce carbon dioxide levels.	☐	☐

Q6 Scientists are researching new ways to **remove** CO_2 from the atmosphere.

a) Use the words below to fill the gaps in the passage.

high	photosynthesis	seeding	hydrocarbons	phytoplankton	injecting

Iron .... involves .... iron into the upper ocean to encourage blooms of .... These blooms remove CO_2 from the atmosphere during .... and so could help to restore the balance. Converting carbon dioxide into .... using .... temperature and pressure, and a catalyst, is another method being researched by scientists.

b) Give **one** possible disadvantage of **one** of the methods described in the passage above.

....

....

Biofuels

Q1   What are **biofuels**?

....

....

Q2   **Biogas** is an example of a biofuel.
The diagram shows the production and use of one type of biogas.

a)   Label the diagram by writing the correct
letter in the boxes next to the arrows:

    A CO_2 released into atmosphere

    B biogas generator

    C animal waste

    D CO_2 absorbed by grass during photosynthesis

    E methane $\rightarrow CO_2$

b)   Explain why biogas is a renewable fuel.

    ....

c)   Suggest why biogas is a fairly cheap fuel.

    ....

    ....

Q3   Indicate by ticking the box whether these statements are **true** or **false**.

		True	False
a)	Ethanol can be used as fuel.	☐	☐
b)	Ethanol is produced by fermenting sugar with yeast.	☐	☐
c)	Ethanol burns to give off toxic gases.	☐	☐
d)	Cars can be adapted to run on a mixture of 50% ethanol and 50% petrol.	☐	☐
e)	It doesn't take any energy to produce ethanol.	☐	☐

Biofuels

Q4   In Brazil, **ethanol** produced by **fermenting sugar cane** is a popular fuel for vehicles. The ethanol is mixed with **petrol** before it is used to give a fuel known as **gasohol**.

a)   What is produced when **ethanol** (C_2H_5OH) is burnt?

....

b)   Using gasohol does not increase the amount of carbon dioxide in the atmosphere as much as using pure petrol does. Explain why not.

....

....

c)   Why would it be more difficult to produce large quantities of gasohol in the UK than it is in Brazil?

....

....

Q5   Alternative fuels such as **biogas** and **gasohol** have advantages and disadvantages compared with traditional fossil fuels.

Imagine you are writing a leaflet for a 'green' organisation promoting the use of alternative fuels like biogas and ethanol instead of fossil fuels.

a)   Give four advantages of these fuels that you could use in favour of your argument.

1. ....

2. ....

3. ....

4. ....

b)   Suggest two points that someone who disagrees with you might put forward.

1. ....

....

2. ....

....

Top Tips: **Reducing CO_2 emissions** isn't all about loving trees and hugging bunnies, but about being sensible. No one wants to go back to living in caves, but we do need to face up to the fact that our modern lifestyle is causing problems. Luckily there might be some real solutions in the pipeline.

42

Fuel Cells

Q1 Hydrogen and oxygen can be used in fuel cells.

a) Draw lines to match the gases with the laboratory tests for them.

| Oxygen | | Relights a glowing splint |

| Hydrogen | | Makes a squeaky pop when burnt |

b) Name the product obtained when hydrogen and oxygen react in a fuel cell.

....

Q2 Use some of the words in the box to complete the passage below.

| fuel | battery | oxygen | electricity | carbon dioxide | walrus |

A fuel cell is an electrical cell that's supplied with a .... and .... and uses energy from the reaction between them to generate ....

Q3 Give three **advantages** and two **disadvantages** of using hydrogen fuel cells compared to alternative energy sources.

Advantages:

1. ....

2. ....

3. ....

Disadvantages:

1. ....

2. ....

Measuring the Energy Content of Fuels

Q1 Isobella is trying to decide which hydrocarbon, A or B, is the best one to use as a fuel. She tests the **energy content** of the hydrocarbons by using them to heat 50 cm³ of water from 25 °C to 40 °C. The results of this experiment are shown in the table.

Hydrocarbon	Initial Mass (g)	Final Mass (g)	Mass of Fuel Burnt (g)
A	98	92	
B	102	89	

a) Complete the table by calculating the mass of fuel that was burned in each case.

b) i) Which hydrocarbon would be the best to use as a fuel?

....

ii) Explain your answer.

....

c) i) The apparatus that Isobella used is shown below. Fill in the missing labels.

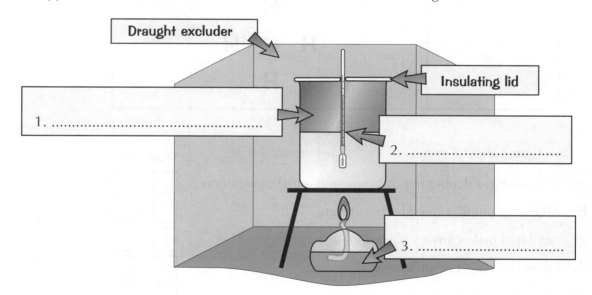

Draught excluder

Insulating lid

1. ....

2. ....

3. ....

ii) Explain the purpose of the draught excluder and the insulating lid in the diagram above.

....

d) Give three things that Isobella should keep **the same** to make sure that her experiment is **fair**.

1. ....

2. ....

3. ....

Alkanes and Alkenes

Q1 **Alkanes** and **alkenes** are both hydrocarbons.

Complete the table below to show the names and displayed formulae of some alkanes and alkenes.

Name	Displayed formula
a)	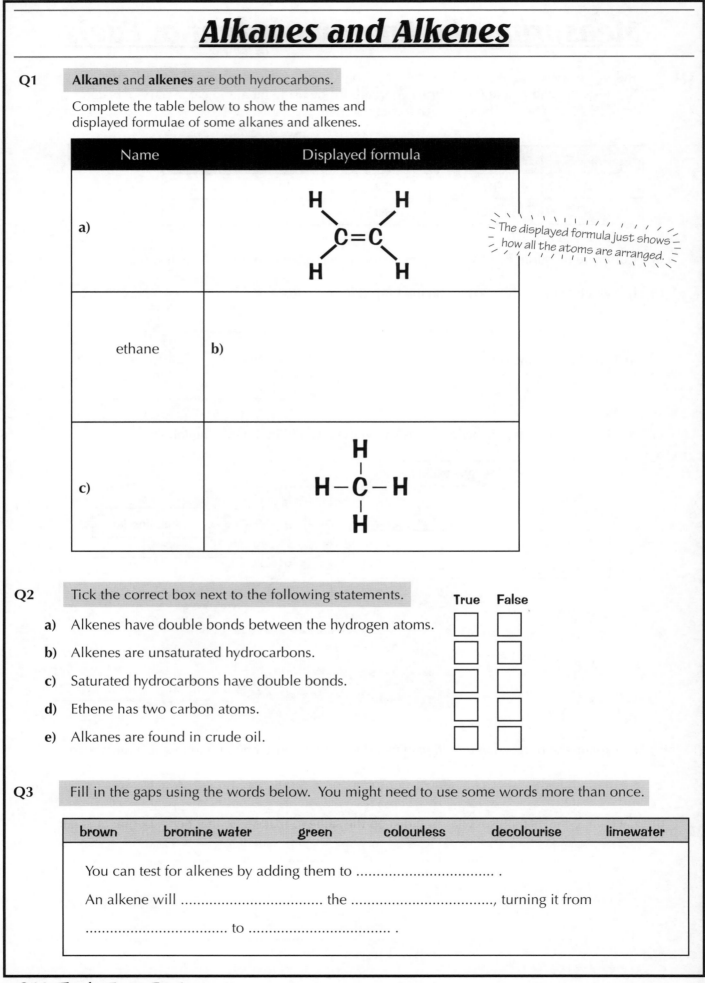
ethane	b)
c)	

The displayed formula just shows how all the atoms are arranged.

Q2 Tick the correct box next to the following statements.

		True	False
a)	Alkenes have double bonds between the hydrogen atoms.	☐	☐
b)	Alkenes are unsaturated hydrocarbons.	☐	☐
c)	Saturated hydrocarbons have double bonds.	☐	☐
d)	Ethene has two carbon atoms.	☐	☐
e)	Alkanes are found in crude oil.	☐	☐

Q3 Fill in the gaps using the words below. You might need to use some words more than once.

brown	bromine water	green	colourless	decolourise	limewater

You can test for alkenes by adding them to ....

An alkene will .... the ...., turning it from

.... to ....

Cracking Hydrocarbons

Q1   Fill in the gaps by choosing from the words in the box.

high	shorter	long	saturated	catalyst	cracking
diesel	molecules	petrol	double bond	alkenes	

There is more need for .... chain fractions of crude oil such as

.... than for longer chains such as ....

Heating .... hydrocarbon molecules to .... temperatures

with a .... breaks them down into smaller ....

This is called .... It also produces .... which are

needed for making plastics.

Q2   This apparatus can be used to crack a **liquid hydrocarbon** such as **paraffin**.

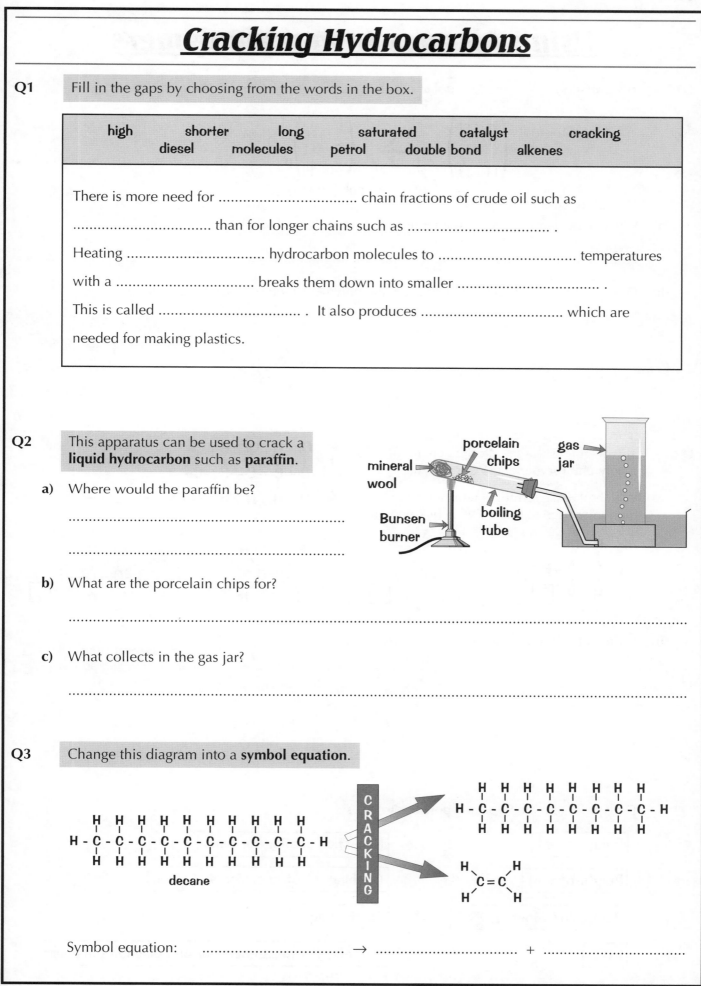

a)   Where would the paraffin be?

....

....

b)   What are the porcelain chips for?

....

c)   What collects in the gas jar?

....

Q3   Change this diagram into a **symbol equation**.

Symbol equation: .... → .... + ...

Using Alkenes to Make Polymers

Q1 The equation below shows a polymerisation reaction to form **poly(ethene)**.

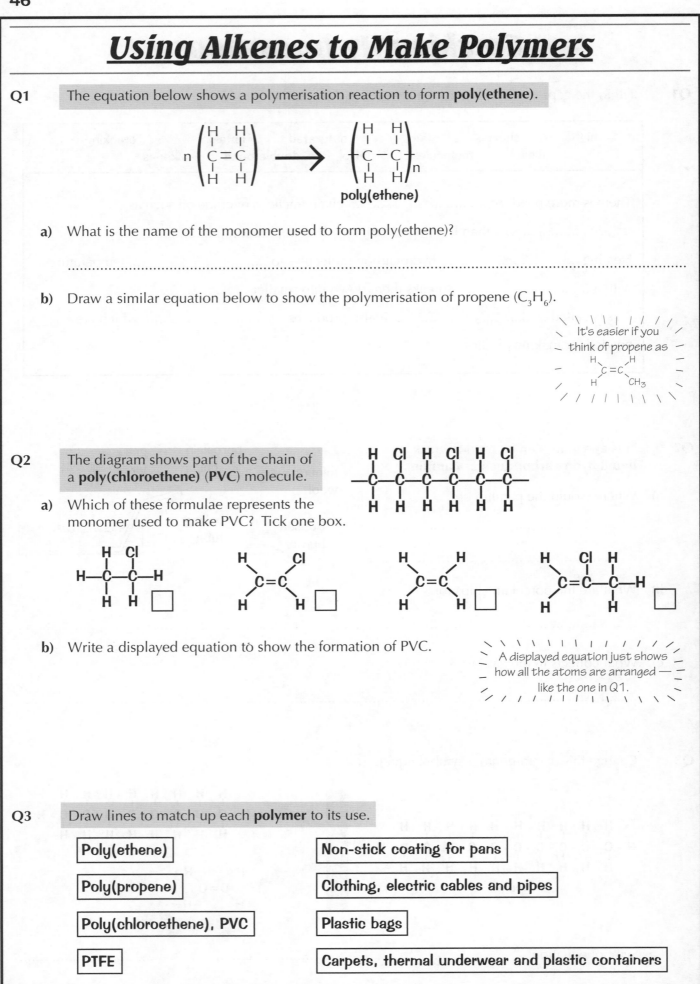

a) What is the name of the monomer used to form poly(ethene)?

....

b) Draw a similar equation below to show the polymerisation of propene (C_3H_6).

It's easier if you think of propene as

Q2 The diagram shows part of the chain of a **poly(chloroethene)** (**PVC**) molecule.

a) Which of these formulae represents the monomer used to make PVC? Tick one box.

b) Write a displayed equation to show the formation of PVC.

A displayed equation just shows how all the atoms are arranged — like the one in Q1.

Q3 Draw lines to match up each **polymer** to its use.

Poly(ethene)	Non-stick coating for pans
Poly(propene)	Clothing, electric cables and pipes
Poly(chloroethene), PVC	Plastic bags
PTFE	Carpets, thermal underwear and plastic containers

Using Alkenes to Make Polymers

Q4 Fractional distillation of crude oil produces useful fractions and not-so-useful fractions.
The not-so-useful ones are **cracked** to form alkenes. Alkenes can be **polymerised** to make plastics.

Write down the differences between cracking and polymerisation.

....

....

....

....

We bring you gold, frankincense...
and poly-myrrh

Q5 Most polymers are **not** biodegradable.

If something's biodegradable it can rot.

a) What problems does this cause for the environment?

....

....

b) What is the problem with burning polymers to dispose of them?

....

c) Give **two** problems with recycling polymers.

1. ....

2. ....

d) Scientists are working on making biodegradable materials from genetically modified plants.
Suggest why tests need to be carried out to find out what happens when the polymer breaks down.

....

....

Top Tips: Sorry, but **polymers** are all over the blooming place, so you're going to have to be clued up about them. It's really no biggie though, because if you think about it, they're just glorified daisy chains. A bunch of silly hydrogen and carbon atoms standing around holding hands with each other — maybe with some chlorine or something as well. What a load of fuss for a plastic cup.

Mixed Questions — C1b Topics 3, 4 & 5

Q1 Metals make up about 80% of all the elements in the periodic table.

a) Read each of the following statements about metals. If the statement is true, tick the box.

☐ Metals are generally strong but also bendy.

☐ Metals corrode when they are oxidised.

☐ Generally, metals have low melting and boiling points.

☐ Properties of a metal can be altered by mixing it with another metal to form an alloy.

b) i) Copper is used for water pipes. Give one reason why it is good for this.

....

....

ii) Give one use of gold and say why it is suitable for this use.

....

....

c) Look at the information in the table below. R, S, T and U are all metals.

Material	Strength	Cost (£)	Density (g/cm³)	Melting Point (°C)
R	High	100	3	1000
S	Medium	90	5	150
T	High	450	8	1200
U	Low	200	11	1070

Explain in detail which material would be most suitable to build an aeroplane body.

....

....

....

Q2 **Biogas** is a renewable fuel.

a) What is biogas made from? ....

b) Explain why burning biogas produces **no net increase** in atmospheric carbon dioxide.

....

....

Mixed Questions — C1b Topics 3, 4 & 5

Q3   **Alkenes** are a type of hydrocarbon.

a) The structural formula for ethene is shown in the box below.
    Draw the structural formula for propene in the other box.

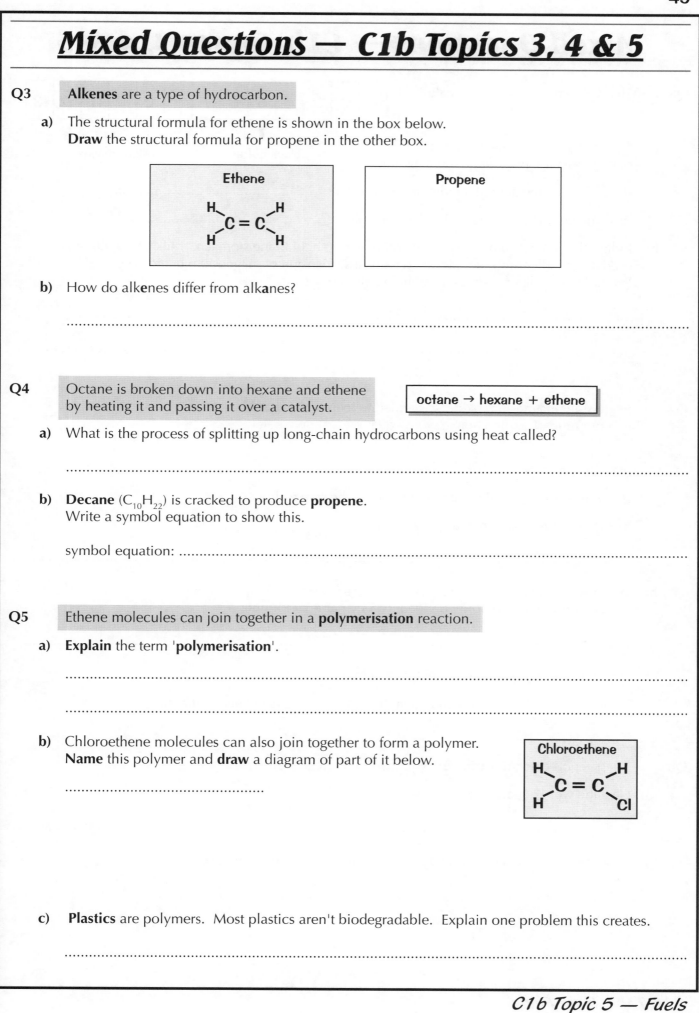

Ethene

Propene

b) How do alkenes differ from alkanes?

....

Q4   Octane is broken down into hexane and ethene by heating it and passing it over a catalyst.

octane → hexane + ethene

a) What is the process of splitting up long-chain hydrocarbons using heat called?

....

b) **Decane** ($C_{10}H_{22}$) is cracked to produce **propene**.
    Write a symbol equation to show this.

    symbol equation: ....

Q5   Ethene molecules can join together in a **polymerisation** reaction.

a) **Explain** the term '**polymerisation**'.

....

....

b) Chloroethene molecules can also join together to form a polymer.
    Name this polymer and **draw** a diagram of part of it below.

    ....

Chloroethene

c) **Plastics** are polymers. Most plastics aren't biodegradable. Explain one problem this creates.

....

Mixed Questions — C1b Topics 3, 4 & 5

Q6 The diagram shows the **pH scale**.

1	2	3	4	5	6	7	8	9	10	11	12	13

↑ black coffee   ↑ milk of magnesia

a) The pH values of black coffee and milk of magnesia are marked on the diagram.

i) Is black coffee neutral, acidic or alkaline? ....

ii) Is milk of magnesia neutral, acidic or alkaline? ....

b) Indigestion is caused by the production of excess acid in the stomach. Milk of magnesia is used as an indigestion remedy. It contains a suspension of magnesium hydroxide, $Mg(OH)_2$. Explain how milk of magnesia can help with indigestion.

....

....

Q7 Some solid **magnesium oxide** was added to **hydrochloric acid** solution in a test tube. The incomplete word equation is shown below.

magnesium oxide + hydrochloric acid → .... + water

a) i) Fill in the name of the missing product in the space above.

ii) What is this type of reaction known as?

....

b) When solid magnesium oxide was added to a substance **S**, magnesium sulfate and water were formed. Identify **S** by name or formula.

....

c) Circle the correct word in the sentence below.

Metal oxides and metal hydroxides are usually **acids / bases**.

Q8 Anass reacts **calcium carbonate** with hydrochloric acid.

a) Give the word equation for this reaction.

....

b) Describe how Anass could test for the gas produced in this reaction.

....

....

Atoms

Q1 Draw a diagram to show the structure of a **helium atom** in the box below. Label each type of **particle** on your diagram.

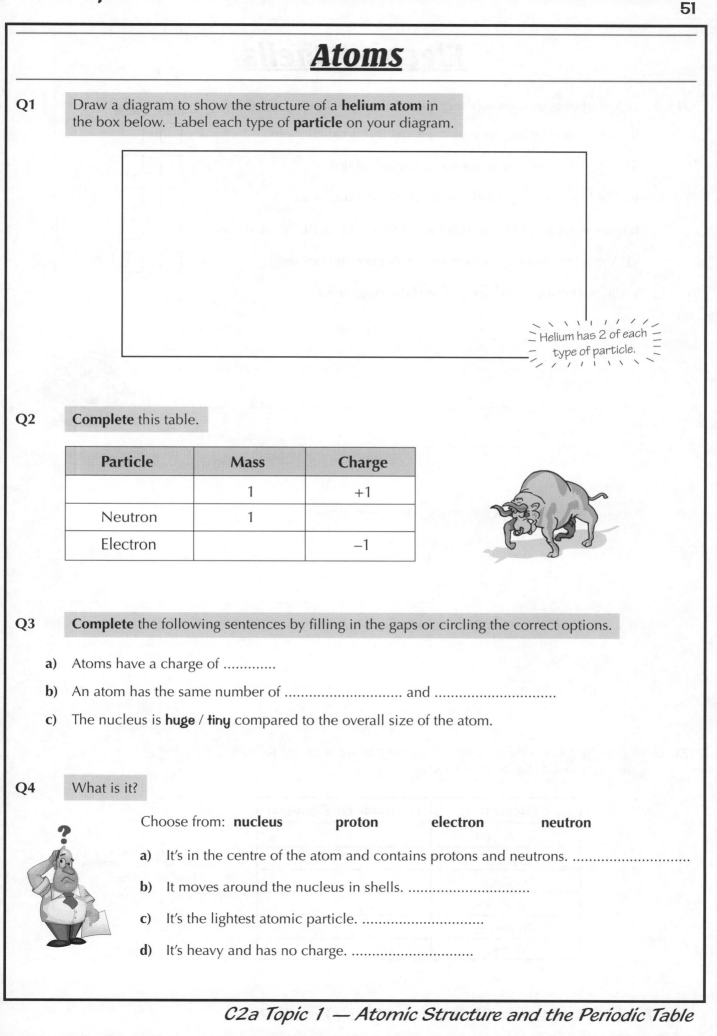

Helium has 2 of each type of particle.

Q2 **Complete** this table.

Particle	Mass	Charge
	1	+1
Neutron	1	
Electron		−1

Q3 **Complete** the following sentences by filling in the gaps or circling the correct options.

a) Atoms have a charge of ....

b) An atom has the same number of .... and ....

c) The nucleus is **huge** / **tiny** compared to the overall size of the atom.

Q4 What is it?

Choose from: **nucleus**   **proton**   **electron**   **neutron**

a) It's in the centre of the atom and contains protons and neutrons. ....

b) It moves around the nucleus in shells. ....

c) It's the lightest atomic particle. ....

d) It's heavy and has no charge. ....

Electron Shells

Q1 a) Tick the boxes to show whether each statement is **true** or **false**.

	True	False
i) Electrons orbit the nucleus in energy levels called shells.	☐	☐
ii) The highest energy levels are always filled first.	☐	☐
iii) The lowest energy levels are closest to the nucleus.	☐	☐
iv) Atoms are less likely to react when they have partially filled shells.	☐	☐
v) A maximum of eight electrons can occupy the first shell.	☐	☐

b) Write out corrected versions of the **false** statements.

....

....

....

....

Q2 Identify **two** things that are wrong with this diagram.

1. ....

....

2. ....

....

Q3 Fill in the table with the **electronic configurations** for the following elements. The first one has been done for you.

Element	Electronic configuration
Beryllium	2.2
Oxygen	
Silicon	
Boron	
Aluminium	
Argon	

You'll need to use the periodic table (at the front of this book) to work out how many electrons each element has.

C2a Topic 1 — Atomic Structure and the Periodic Table

Electron Shells

Q4   **Chlorine** has 17 protons.

a)   What is its electronic configuration? ....

b)   Draw the electrons on the shells in the diagram.

c)   Why does chlorine react readily?

....

Q5   Draw the **full electronic configurations** for these elements. (The first three have been done for you.)

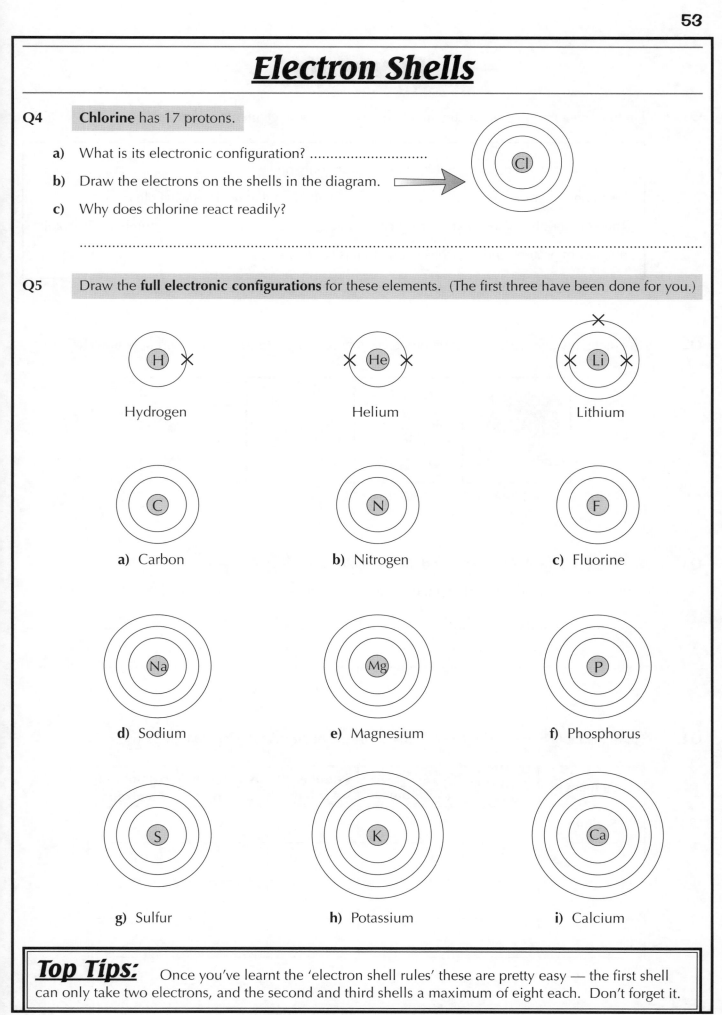

Hydrogen   Helium   Lithium

a) Carbon   b) Nitrogen   c) Fluorine

d) Sodium   e) Magnesium   f) Phosphorus

g) Sulfur   h) Potassium   i) Calcium

Top Tips: Once you've learnt the 'electron shell rules' these are pretty easy — the first shell can only take two electrons, and the second and third shells a maximum of eight each. Don't forget it.

Elements

Q1   Fill in the blanks to complete the following passage about **elements** and **atoms**.

An element is a substance that is made up from only one type of ....

It's the number of .... in an atom that decides what element it is.

The number of protons in an atom is called the .... number. The total

number of protons and neutrons in an atom is called the .... number.

Q2   The diagrams below show four different substances. Circle those that contain only **one element**.

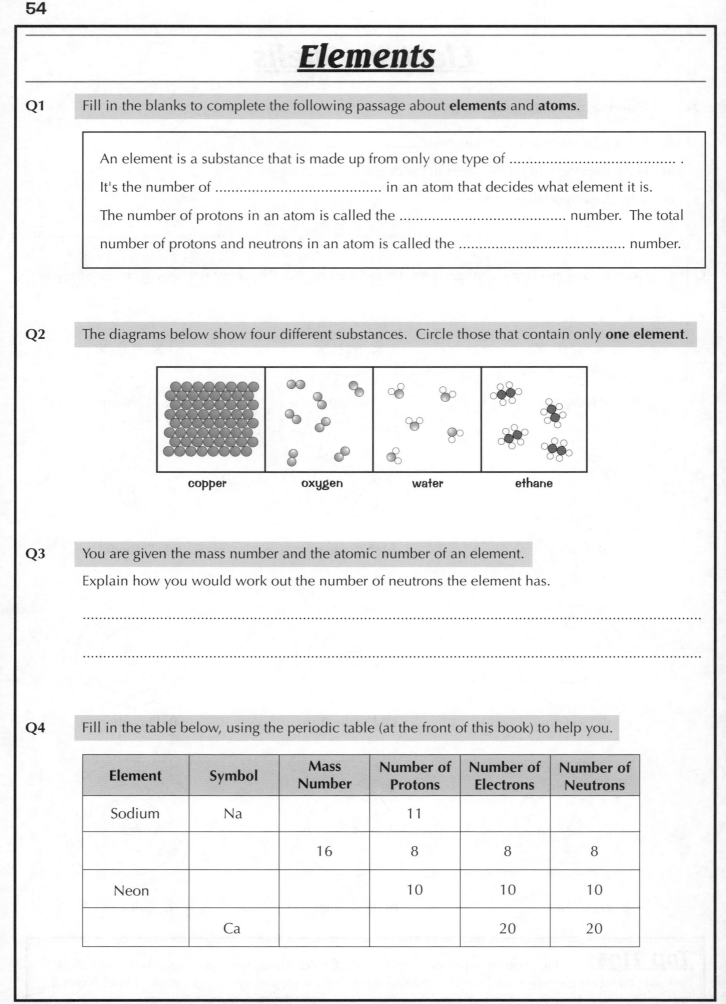

| copper | oxygen | water | ethane |

Q3   You are given the mass number and the atomic number of an element.

Explain how you would work out the number of neutrons the element has.

....

....

Q4   Fill in the table below, using the periodic table (at the front of this book) to help you.

Element	Symbol	Mass Number	Number of Protons	Number of Electrons	Number of Neutrons
Sodium	Na		11		
		16	8	8	8
Neon			10	10	10
	Ca			20	20

Isotopes and Relative Atomic Mass

Q1 Choose the correct words to **complete** this paragraph.

electrons	element	isotopes	protons	compound	neutrons

.... are different atomic forms of the same .... which have

the same number of .... but a different number of ....

Q2 Which of the following atoms are **isotopes** of each other? Explain your answer.

W $_{6}^{12}C$ **X** $_{18}^{40}Ar$ **Y** $_{6}^{14}C$ **Z** $_{20}^{40}Ca$

Answer .... and ....

Explanation ....

....

Q3 Draw lines to join the beginning of each sentence to its correct ending.

Relative atomic mass means

Relative abundance means

how much there is of each isotope compared to the total amount of the element in the world.

the average mass of the atoms of that element including the isotopes.

Q4 **Chlorine** has two main **isotopes**, ^{35}Cl and ^{37}Cl. Their relative abundances are shown in the table.

relative mass of isotope	relative abundance
35	3
37	1

Use this information to calculate the relative atomic mass of chlorine.

....

....

A Brief History of the Periodic Table

Q1 Fill in the gaps using the words provided to complete the following passage.

properties	reactivity series	table	atomic number

Mendeleev attempted to classify all known elements by arranging

them in a .... He used their

.... to do this.

Q2 Tick the boxes to show whether the following statements about **Mendeleev** are **true** or **false**.

True False

a) i) Mendeleev was able to predict the properties of undiscovered elements. ☐ ☐

ii) Mendeleev put elements with similar properties in the same rows. ☐ ☐

b) Write out the corrected version of any **false** statements below.

....

....

Q3 Mendeleev left gaps in his table. He then predicted the discovery of an element that would fill a gap in his Group 4, and called it '**ekasilicon**'.

a) Explain why Mendeleev had to leave gaps in his table.

....

....

b) The table below shows the **densities** of known elements in Mendeleev's Group 4.

'Ekasilicon' was eventually discovered and given another name. Use the table to decide which of the elements below is ekasilicon. Circle your choice.

Element	Density g/cm³
carbon	2.27
silicon	2.33
ekasilicon	
tin	7.31
lead	11.3

palladium, 12.0 g/cm³

beryllium, 1.85 g/cm³

germanium, 5.32 g/cm³

copper, 8.92 g/cm³

Top Tips: As new elements were discovered, Mendeleev's table grew to become the periodic table we still use today. That makes him a bit of a legend in the wonderful world of chemists.

C2a Topic 1 — Atomic Structure and the Periodic Table

The Periodic Table

Q1 Choose from the words in the box to fill in the blanks in the sentences below.

> left   metals   vertical   right   similar   non-metals   horizontal   different

a) A period in the periodic table is a .... row of elements.

b) Most of the elements in the periodic table are ....

c) Non-metals are found on the .... side of the periodic table.

d) Elements in the same group have .... properties.

Q2 Tick the correct boxes to show whether the following statements are **true** or **false**.

		True	False
a)	Elements in a group have the same number of electrons in their outer shells.	☐	☐
b)	The periodic table shows the elements in order of descending atomic number.	☐	☐
c)	Each horizontal row in the periodic table contains elements with similar properties.	☐	☐
d)	The periodic table includes all the known compounds.	☐	☐

Q3 **Argon** is an extremely unreactive gas. Use the periodic table to name two more elements that you would expect to have **similar properties** to argon.

1. ....   2. ....

Q4 Use a **periodic table** to help you answer the following questions.

a) Name one element in the same period as silicon. ....

b) Name one element in the same group as potassium. ....

c) Name one element that has 2 electrons in its outer shell. ....

Q5 **Fluorine** is a member of Group 7.

a) How many electrons does a fluorine atom have in its outer shell? ....

b) Explain why the only information you need to work this out is the group number.

....

Ionic Bonding

Q1 Choose the correct words from the list below to complete the passage.

elements	ionic	atoms	anions	compounds	cations

Atoms of different .... can form chemical bonds and join together

to create new .... One way they can do this is by ....

bonding. Electrons are transferred between atoms so they form ....

and ....

Q2 Tick one of the boxes below to show which statement is the best definition of an **ion**.

An ion is a compound that contains both positive and negative charges. ☐

An ion is a positively or negatively charged atom or group of atoms. ☐

An ion is a positively or negatively charged element. ☐

Q3 Tick the correct boxes to show whether the
statements below are **true** or **false**.

                                                       True   **False**

a) In ionic bonding, ions lose or gain electrons to become atoms. ☐ ☐

b) Ions with opposite charges attract each other. ☐ ☐

c) Elements that lose electrons form positive ions. ☐ ☐

d) Elements that gain electrons form cations. ☐ ☐

e) Atoms form ions so that they can have full outer shells. ☐ ☐

Q4 Use the **diagram** to answer the following questions.

a) Which group of the periodic table does sodium belong to? ....

b) How many electrons does chlorine need to gain in order to have a full outer shell? ....

c) What is the charge on a sodium ion? ....

Ionic Bonding

Q5 Elements react in order to get a **full outer shell** of electrons.

a) How many electrons does magnesium need to **lose** to get a full outer shell? ....

b) How many electrons does oxygen need to **gain** to get a full outer shell? ....

c) Draw a 'dot and cross' diagram in the space provided to show what happens to the outer shells of electrons when magnesium and oxygen react.

> The diagrams in question 4 on the previous page are 'dot and cross' diagrams.

Q6 Atoms can **gain** or **lose** electrons to get a full outer shell.

a) How many electrons do the following elements need to **lose** in order to get a **full outer shell**?

i) Lithium ....   ii) Calcium ....   iii) Potassium ....

b) How many electrons do the following elements need to **gain** in order to get a **full outer shell**?

i) Oxygen ....   ii) Chlorine ....   iii) Fluorine ....

Q7 **Beryllium** is in **Group 2** of the periodic table.
Complete the following sentences by circling the correct word from each pair.

a) An atom of beryllium has **two** / **six** electrons in its outer shell.

b) It will form an ion by **gaining** / **losing** electrons.

c) The charge on a beryllium ion will be **2$^+$** / **2$^-$**.

d) A beryllium ion is **an anion** / **a cation**.

e) Beryllium **can** / **can't** form ionic bonds with elements from Group 1.

f) Beryllium **can** / **can't** form ionic bonds with elements from Group 6.

Ionic Compounds

Q1 Use a 'dot and cross' diagram to show what happens to the outer shells of electrons when **sodium** and **oxygen** react to give **sodium oxide**.

Q2 Explain how sodium and chlorine atoms react to form the ionic compound **sodium chloride**.

....

....

Q3 Use 'dot and cross' diagrams showing the outer shells of electrons to explain why potassium chloride has the formula **KCl** but magnesium chloride has the formula **MgCl$_2$**.

Ionic Compounds

Q4   **Sodium chloride** is an ionic compound.

a)   Circle the statement from the list below that **best** describes the **structure** of sodium chloride.

A regular lattice arrangement.   A cube.   A chain of positive and negative ions.

b)   Circle the correct words to explain why sodium chloride has a **high melting point**.

> Sodium chloride has very **strong** / **weak** electrostatic forces of attraction between
> the **negative** / **positive** sodium ions and the **negative** / **positive** chloride ions.
> This means that it needs a **small** / **large** amount of energy to break the bonds.

Q5   Mike carries out an experiment to find out if **magnesium oxide** conducts electricity.
He tests the compound when it's solid, when it's dissolved in water and when it's molten.

a)   Complete the following table of results.

	Conducts electricity? (Yes / No)
When solid	
When dissolved in water	
When molten	

b)   Explain your answers to part **a)**.

....

....

....

Q6   The melting point of **calcium chloride** is **772 °C** and that of **carbon chloride** is **−23 °C**.

Which one is an ionic compound? Explain your choice.

....

....

....

Top Tips: Ionic bonds are a bit of a one-trick pony — they always produce compounds with a
similar structure. So, once you've learnt that structure you can apply it to any ionic compound.

Naming Compounds and Finding Formulas

Q1 The names of compounds can tell us what **elements** they contain.

a) Use options from the box below to complete the passage about naming compounds.

oxygen	-IDE	hydrogen	-ATE	two	one	-ADE

When .... elements combine the compound's name is

'something ....'. When three or more different elements

combine and one of them is .... the compound's name is

'something ....'.

b) i) Which elements are present in potassium nitrate?

....

ii) Which elements are present in calcium carbonate?

....

Q2 Here are some elements and the **ions** they form:

Make sure the charges on the ions balance.

beryllium, Be^{2+}   **potassium, K$^+$**   **iodine, I$^-$**   **sulfur, S^{2-}**

Write down the formulas of four compounds which can be made using these elements.

1. ....   3. ....

2. ....   4. ....

Q3 Give the **formulas** of the following ionic compounds.
Use the table on the right to help.

a) potassium bromide ....

b) iron(II) chloride ....

c) calcium fluoride ....

d) sodium carbonate ....

e) iron(III) sulfate ....

Positive Ions		Negative Ions	
Sodium	Na$^+$	Chloride	Cl$^-$
Potassium	K$^+$	Fluoride	F$^-$
Calcium	Ca^{2+}	Bromide	Br$^-$
Iron(II)	Fe^{2+}	Carbonate	CO$_3^{2-}$
Iron(III)	Fe^{3+}	Sulfate	SO$_4^{2-}$

Q4 The formula of calcium nitrate is **Ca(NO$_3$)$_2$**.

The charge on the calcium ion is 2+. State the charge on the nitrate ion. ....

Preparing Insoluble Salts

Q1 **A**, **B** and **C** are symbol equations for reactions in which **salts** are formed.

    A $\quad CuO(s) + H_2SO_4(aq) \rightarrow CuSO_4(aq) + H_2O(l)$

    B $\quad 2NaOH(aq) + H_2SO_4(aq) \rightarrow Na_2SO_4(aq) + 2H_2O(l)$

    C $\quad Pb(NO_3)_2(aq) + H_2SO_4(aq) \rightarrow PbSO_4(s) + 2HNO_3(aq)$

Which equation (A, B or C) shows the formation of an insoluble salt by a precipitation reaction?

....

Q2 **Silver chloride** is an insoluble salt which is formed as a **precipitate** when silver nitrate and sodium chloride solutions are mixed together.

a) Complete the word equation for the reaction.

.... + ... → silver chloride + ...

b) After mixing the solutions to produce a precipitate, what further steps are needed to produce a dry sample of silver chloride?

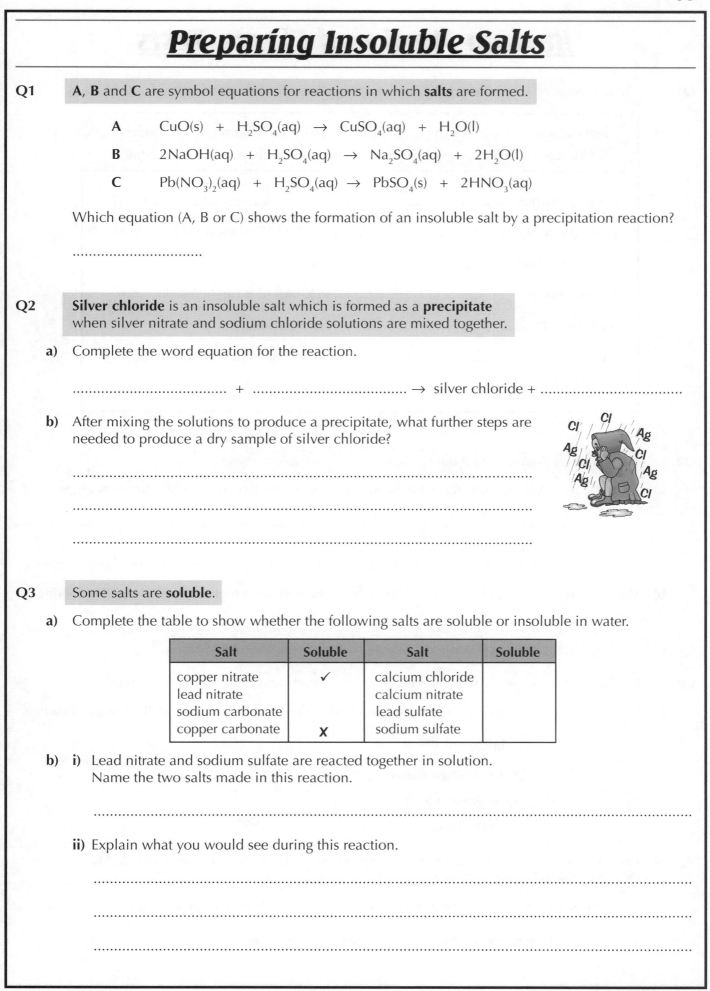

....

....

....

Q3 Some salts are **soluble**.

a) Complete the table to show whether the following salts are soluble or insoluble in water.

Salt	Soluble	Salt	Soluble
copper nitrate	✓	calcium chloride	
lead nitrate		calcium nitrate	
sodium carbonate		lead sulfate	
copper carbonate	✗	sodium sulfate	

b) i) Lead nitrate and sodium sulfate are reacted together in solution. Name the two salts made in this reaction.

....

ii) Explain what you would see during this reaction.

....

....

....

Barium Meal and Flame Tests

Q1   Choose from the words below to complete the passage about barium sulfate.

bloodstream	toxic	insoluble	meal	soluble
blockages	invisible	gut	drink	opaque

Although barium salts are ...., barium sulfate can be

safely drunk because it is .... This means that it passes

through the body without being absorbed into the ....

Barium sulfate is .... to X-rays so it can be used to show

up a patient's .... This means that any problems

e.g. .... can be seen. Drinking barium before an X-ray

is known as a barium ....

Q2   **Flame tests** are often carried out to identify unknown substances.

a)   Describe how you would carry out a flame test using a wire loop on an unknown powder.

....

....

b)   Why would the results of this test be unreliable if the wire loop had not been cleaned properly?

....

Q3   Les had four samples of **metal compounds**. He carried out a flame test on each one.

a)   Draw lines to match each of Les's observations to the metal cation producing the coloured flame.

brick-red flame Na^+

yellow/orange flame Cu^{2+}

blue-green flame K^+

lilac flame Ca^{2+}

b)   Les wants to make a firework which will explode in his local football team's colour, **lilac**.
Which of the following compounds should he use? Circle your answer.

silver nitrate   sodium chloride   barium sulfate

potassium nitrate   calcium carbonate

C2a Topic 2 — Ionic Compounds and Analysis

Testing for Negative Ions and Spectroscopy

Q1   Choose from the words given to complete the passage below.

carbon dioxide	limewater	acid	sodium hydroxide	hydrogen

Reacting an unidentified substance with dilute .... is a way of testing

for carbonate ions. If they are present then .... will be formed.

You can test for this by bubbling it through .... to see if it becomes milky.

Q2   Answer the following questions on testing for **sulfate** ions.

a)   Which two **chemicals** are used to test for sulfate ions?

....

b)   What would you **see** after adding these chemicals to a sulfate compound?

....

Q3   Deirdre wants to find out if a soluble compound contains **chloride** ions.
Explain how she could do this.

....

....

....

Q4   Complete the following equations for **tests for negative ions**.

a) $Ag^+_{(aq)} + ... \rightarrow AgCl_{(s)}$

b) $2HCl_{(aq)} + Na_2CO_{3(s)} \rightarrow 2NaCl_{(aq)} + ..._{(l)} + ..._{(g)}$

c) $............... + ... \rightarrow BaSO_{4(s)}$

You're being a bit negative today, aren't you?

No...

Q5   Spectroscopy is an **analytical technique** used in laboratories.

a)   Name two elements that were discovered using spectroscopy.

1. ....   2. ....

b)   Give one advantage of using spectroscopy to identify elements.

....

C2a Topic 2 — Ionic Compounds and Analysis

Covalent Bonding

Q1   Indicate whether each statement is **true** or **false**.

True False

a)   Covalent bonding involves sharing one or more pairs of electrons.   ☐ ☐

b)   Atoms react to gain a full outer shell of electrons.   ☐ ☐

c)   When atoms make covalent bonds they form molecules.   ☐ ☐

d)   Hydrogen can form two covalent bonds.   ☐ ☐

e)   Carbon can form four covalent bonds.   ☐ ☐

Q2   **Complete** the following table to show how many electrons are needed to **fill up** the **outer shell** of these atoms.

Atom	Carbon	Chlorine	Hydrogen	Nitrogen	Oxygen
Number of electrons needed to fill outer shell					

Q3   Complete the following diagrams by adding the **electrons**. Only the outer shells are shown.

a)   Hydrogen chloride (HCl)

d)   Carbon dioxide (CO_2)

b)   Oxygen (O_2)

e)   Methane (CH_4)

c)   Water (H_2O)

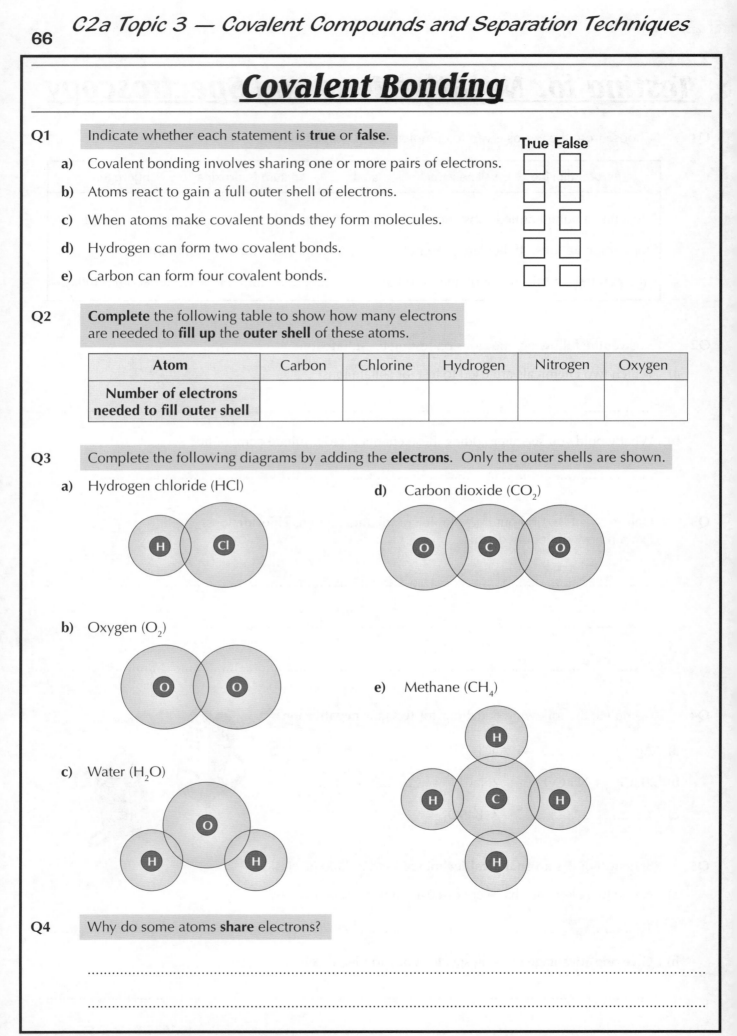

Q4   Why do some atoms **share** electrons?

....

....

Covalent Substances — Two Kinds

Q1 Fill in the blanks in the following paragraph by choosing words from the list.

weak	hard	small	easy	large	strong

Simple molecular covalent substances are made from .... molecules.

The covalent bonds that hold the atoms together are .... but the forces

between the molecules are quite .... Because of this it is fairly

.... to separate the molecules.

Q2 Complete the following sentences by circling the correct option, and explain your answers.

a) The melting and boiling points of simple molecular covalent substances are **low** / **high**.

....

b) Simple molecular covalent substances **conduct** / **don't conduct** electricity.

....

Q3 Circle the correct words to complete the following paragraph.

Giant molecular covalent structures contain **charged ions** / **uncharged atoms**. The covalent bonds

between the atoms are **strong** / **weak**. Giant molecular covalent structures have **high** / **low** melting

points and they are usually **soluble** / **insoluble** in water.

Q4 **Graphite** and **diamond** are both made entirely from **carbon**, but have different properties.

a) Explain why graphite's structure makes it a good material for making electrodes.

....

....

b) Explain how diamond's structure makes it useful for use in drill tips.

....

....

c) Explain why graphite's structure makes it a good lubricant, but diamond's structure doesn't.

....

....

Classifying Elements and Compounds

Q1   Complete the following table by placing a **tick** or a **cross** in each box.

Property	Ionic Lattice	Giant Molecular	Simple Molecular
High melting and boiling points			
Can conduct electricity when solid		except graphite	
Can conduct electricity when molten		except graphite	

Q2   The table gives data for some **physical properties** of a selection of elements and compounds.

substance	state at room temp	melting point / °C	boiling point / °C	electrical conductivity solid	electrical conductivity liquid
A	solid	114	184	poor	poor
B	gas	-73	-10	poor	poor
C	solid	3550	4827	poor	poor
D	solid	858	1505	poor	good
E	solid	1495	2870	good	good
F	liquid	0	50	poor	poor

a) **i)** Identify one substance that is **likely** to have a **simple molecular** structure. ....

  ii) Explain your answer.

  ....

  ....

  ....

b) **i)** Which of the substances is **most likely** to have a **giant molecular** structure? ....

  ii) Explain your answer.

  ....

  ....

  ....

Top Tips: Chemists spend a lot of time identifying substances. Hiding behind those safety goggles there's a frustrated detective trying to get out. Anyway, the bottom line is that you need to be able to work out whether a substance is an ionic lattice, giant molecular or simple molecular. The clues are boiling point, melting point and electrical conductivity. Go get 'em Sherlock.

Separation Techniques

Q1   Some liquid mixtures are **immiscible** and some are **miscible**.

a)   Draw lines to match the type of mixture to its description and separation method.

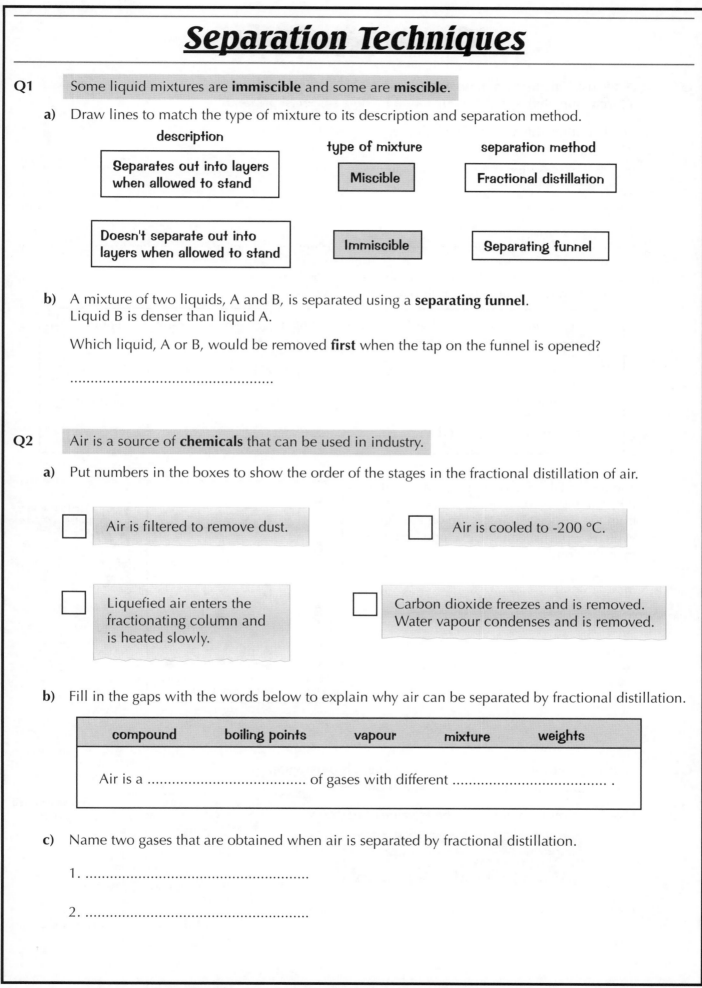

description

| Separates out into layers when allowed to stand |

type of mixture

| Miscible |

separation method

| Fractional distillation |

| Doesn't separate out into layers when allowed to stand |

| Immiscible |

| Separating funnel |

b)   A mixture of two liquids, A and B, is separated using a **separating funnel**.
Liquid B is denser than liquid A.

Which liquid, A or B, would be removed **first** when the tap on the funnel is opened?

....

Q2   Air is a source of **chemicals** that can be used in industry.

a)   Put numbers in the boxes to show the order of the stages in the fractional distillation of air.

☐   Air is filtered to remove dust.

☐   Air is cooled to -200 °C.

☐   Liquefied air enters the fractionating column and is heated slowly.

☐   Carbon dioxide freezes and is removed. Water vapour condenses and is removed.

b)   Fill in the gaps with the words below to explain why air can be separated by fractional distillation.

compound	boiling points	vapour	mixture	weights

Air is a .... of gases with different ....

c)   Name two gases that are obtained when air is separated by fractional distillation.

1. ....

2. ....

Chromatography

Q1 Ella is using **paper chromatography** to compare the **ink** used on a **threatening letter** with the ink found in three **suspects' printers**.

I'm gonna mess you up big style.

Y

a) Briefly outline the method Ella will use.

....

....

....

b) Using words from the list below, complete the following passage to describe how paper chromatography works.

chromatogram	solvent	lines	filter	graph	ink	spots

The .... seeps up the paper taking the samples of inks with it.

The different chemicals in the inks form separate .... on the

paper. This result is called a ....

c) The results Ella gets when she analyses the ink from the threatening letter and the ink from the suspects' printers are on the right. Which suspect(s) can she **exclude** from the investigation?

....

I'll get you and your little dog.

K

I know where you live.

C

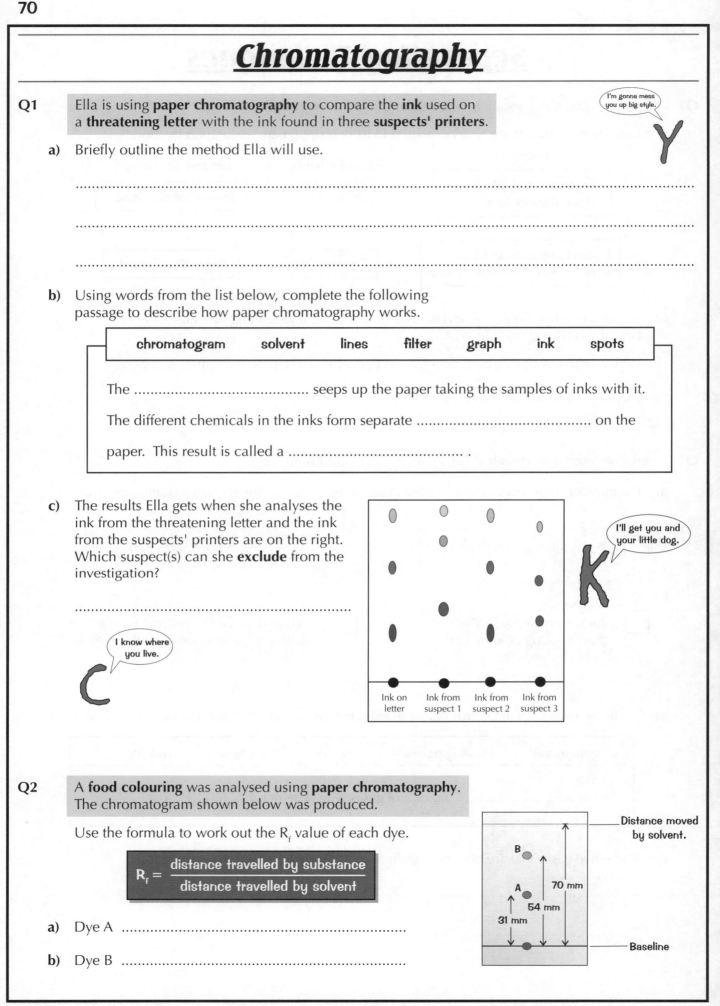

Ink on letter — Ink from suspect 1 — Ink from suspect 2 — Ink from suspect 3

Q2 A **food colouring** was analysed using **paper chromatography**. The chromatogram shown below was produced.

Use the formula to work out the R_f value of each dye.

$$R_f = \frac{\text{distance travelled by substance}}{\text{distance travelled by solvent}}$$

Distance moved by solvent.

B

A

70 mm

54 mm

31 mm

Baseline

a) Dye A ....

b) Dye B ....

Mixed Questions — C2a Topics 1, 2 & 3

Q1 Answer the following questions about the **periodic table**.

a) If an element is in Group 1, how many electrons will it have in its outer electron shell? ....

b) An ion of an element has a 2+ charge. Which group is the element **most likely** to be in? ....

c) If an ion has a 1– charge, then which group is it **most likely** to be in? ....

You can use the periodic table (at the front of this book) to help you.

d) Complete this table by filling in the **electronic configurations** of the elements:

Period	Group 1	Group 2	Group 3	Group 7	Group 0
2	Li 2.1	Be	B	F	Ne
3	Na	Mg	Al	Cl	Ar 2.8.8

Q2 Hydrogen atoms can exist as three **isotopes** — ^{1}H (hydrogen), ^{2}H (deuterium) and ^{3}H (tritium).

a) What is an isotope?

....

....

b) Explain why the relative atomic mass of an element isn't always a whole number.

....

....

c) Complete the table.

isotope	number of protons	number of neutrons	number of electrons
^{1}H			
^{2}H			
^{3}H			

d) The atomic number is often left out of the isotope symbol.
For instance, it is acceptable to write ^{12}**C** for carbon-12 rather than $^{12}_6$**C**.

i) Define the term **atomic number**.

....

ii) Explain why the atomic number can be left out of the isotope symbol.

....

....

Mixed Questions — C2a Topics 1, 2 & 3

Q3   Stanley is trying to identify a mystery substance.

First he dips a clean wire loop in the substance and puts it in a Bunsen flame.

a)   What result would you expect Stanley to see if the mystery compound contained Ca^{2+} ions?

....

...and add a splash of $CaSO_4$, with a dollop of $MgBr_2$ and a dash of Worcester sauce...

b)   In fact, he sees a blue-green flame. What can Stanley conclude?

....

c)   Stanley suspects that his compound is a sulfate. Describe a test he could do to see if he's right.

....

....

d)   Stanley does the test for a sulfate, and sees a white precipitate form in the solution.

  i)   Write down an **ionic equation** for the formation of this white precipitate. Include state symbols.

....

  ii)   Write down the formula of Stanley's mystery compound. ....

Q4   **Lithium** is a metallic element in **Group 1** of the periodic table.

a)   Draw a diagram to show the electronic configuration in a lithium atom.

Use the periodic table to help you.

b)   **Fluorine** is in **Group 7** of the periodic table. Its electronic configuration is shown below.

  i)   Give the chemical formula for the compound that forms between lithium and fluorine.

....

  ii)   What type of bonding is involved in this compound? ....

Properties of Metals

Q1   Most **metals** that are used to make everyday objects are found in the **central section** of the periodic table.

a) What name is given to this group of metals?

....

b) What property of a typical metal from this group would make it suitable for electrical wires?

....

c) Give one property of compounds formed by these metals.

....

Q2   All metals have a similar **structure**. This explains why many of them have similar **properties**.

a) Draw a labelled diagram showing the structure of a typical metal.

Think about the reason why metals are good conductors.

b) What is unusual about the electrons in a metal?

....

Q3   Imagine that a space probe has brought a sample of a new element back from Mars. Scientists think that the element is a **metal**, but they aren't certain. Give **three properties** they could look for to provide evidence that the element is a **metal**.

1. ....

2. ....

3. ....

Top Tips: Remember, most elements are metals and most metals have similar properties. This is because all metals have a similar structure. But don't go thinking that they're all identical — there are lots of little differences which make them useful for different things.

Group 1 — The Alkali Metals

Q1   **Sodium**, **potassium** and **lithium** are all alkali metals.

a)   Highlight the location of the alkali metals
on this periodic table.

b)   State two physical properties of alkali metals.

1. ....

2. ....

c)   Put sodium, potassium and lithium in order of increasing reactivity with water.

least reactive   ....

....

most reactive   ....

d)   Explain why the alkali metals become more reactive as their atomic number increases.

....

....

....

Q2   Three different **alkali metals**, A, B and C,
were dropped into bowls of water. The time
taken for each piece to **vanish** was recorded
and is shown in the table.

METAL	TIME TAKEN TO VANISH (s)
A	27
B	8
C	42

a)   i)   Which of these is the most reactive metal?
How can you tell?

....

....

ii)   The three metals used were lithium, sodium and potassium.
Use the results shown in the table to match them up to the correct letters A, B and C.

A = ...   B = ...   C = ...

b)   i)   What products would be formed in a reaction between sodium and water?

....

ii)   "The amount of time taken for rubidium to vanish in water will be shorter than metal A,
but longer than metal B". Is this statement correct? Explain your answer.

....

....

Group 1 — The Alkali Metals

Q3   Complete the passage using some of the words from the box below.

two   potassium   one   oxygen   hydroxide   hydrogen   carbonate
Potassium is a soft metal with .... electron(s) in its outer shell.   It reacts vigorously with water, producing ....   and .... gas.

Q4   A piece of **lithium** was put into a beaker of water.

a)   Write a word equation for the reaction that occurs.

....

b)   Write a balanced symbol equation for the reaction that occurs.

....

c)   Circle the word in the list below that describes the solution formed at the end of the reaction.

   acidic   **neutral**   **alkaline**

Q5   **Caesium** and **francium** are alkali metals.

a) i)   Look at the periodic table. Which metal would you expect to be more reactive?

   ....

ii)   Explain your answer.

   ....

   ....

b)   Both caesium and francium must be stored in oil. Suggest why this is.

   ....

   ....

Top Tips: Make sure that when it comes to your exam, you're all clued up on the alkali metals. You need to know where they are in the periodic table, and what goes on in their reactions with water. Make sure you know about how their reactivity changes as you go down the group too.

Group 7 — The Halogens

Q1   Highlight the location of the halogens in this periodic table.

Q2   Draw lines to match the halogens to their **descriptions** and **reactivity**.

HALOGEN	DESCRIPTION	REACTIVITY
bromine	green gas	most reactive
chlorine	grey solid	least reactive
iodine	orange liquid	quite reactive

Q3   Tick the correct boxes to say whether these statements are **true** or **false**.

                                                                True   False

a)   Chlorine gas is made up of molecules which each contain three chlorine atoms.

b)   Chlorine reacts with potassium to form an ionic compound.

c)   The halogens become less reactive as you go down the group.

d)   The halogens can lose electrons to form halide ions.

e)   When a more reactive halogen reacts with a solution containing halide ions and pushes out the less reactive halogen, this reaction is called a precipitation reaction.

Q4   Halogens react with hydrogen to form **hydrogen halides**.

a)   State the name of the compound formed when chlorine reacts with hydrogen.

....

b)   The product of the reaction between chlorine and hydrogen is dissolved in water. Is the solution acidic or alkaline?

....

Group 7 — The Halogens

Q5 Halogens can react with **metals** to form salts.

a) What is the general name given to the salts formed by the reaction of a halogen with a metal?

....

b) Fill in the blanks in the following equations.

i) .... + bromine → aluminium bromide

ii) Potassium + ... → potassium iodide

iii) Magnesium + fluorine → ....

c) Write balanced symbol equations for each of the reactions in part **b)**, using the formulas given in the box below.

Mg	Br_2	KI	Al	$AlBr_3$	K	F_2	I_2	MgF_2

i) ....

ii) ....

iii) ....

Q6 Equal volumes of **bromine water** were added to three test tubes, each containing a different **halogen salt solution**. The results are shown in the table.

SOLUTION	RESULT
potassium chloride	no reaction
potassium bromide	no reaction
potassium iodide	reaction

a) Explain why there was no reaction when bromine water was added to potassium chloride solution.

....

....

b) Explain why there was a reaction when bromine water was added to potassium iodide solution.

....

....

....

c) Write a symbol equation for the reaction which took place in the potassium iodide solution when bromine water was added.

....

Group 0 — The Noble Gases

Q1 Where are the noble gases located in the periodic table?

....

Q2 Complete the table using the numbers provided to show trends in the **boiling points** and **densities** of the noble gases.

0.0018

-246

-186

0.0002

Element	Boiling point (°C)	Density (g/cm³)
Helium	-269	
Neon		0.0009
Argon		

Q3 The noble gases were **discovered** long after many of the other elements.

a) Why did it take scientists so long to discover the noble gases?

....

....

b) Circle the correct words to complete the passage below.

The noble gases were eventually discovered when scientists noticed that the density

of nitrogen made in **chemical reactions / fractional distillation** was different to the density

of nitrogen taken from **water / air** . They suggested that the nitrogen from the **water / air**

must have other **metals / gases** mixed in with it. Scientists used **fractional distillation /**

displacement reactions to separate the noble gases from the nitrogen.

c) Explain why the noble gases are unreactive.

....

....

....

Top Tips: The examiners will expect you to know quite a bit about certain groups in the periodic table — the halogens, the alkali metals, the noble gases and the transition metals. Make sure you're clear on their general properties and how these change as you move down or up each group.

Energy Transfer in Reactions

Q1 Chemical reactions may be **exothermic** or **endothermic**.

a) Circle the correct words in this paragraph about **exothermic** reactions.

Exothermic reactions **take in** / **give out** energy overall, in the form of **heat** / **sound**.
This is shown by a **fall** / **rise** in **temperature** / **mass**.

b) Tick the correct boxes to indicate whether the following reactions are exothermic or endothermic.

	Exothermic	Endothermic
i) Photosynthesis	☐	☐
ii) Combustion	☐	☐
iii) An explosion	☐	☐
iv) Dissolving ammonium nitrate in water	☐	☐

Q2 Fill in the missing words in this paragraph about **endothermic** reactions to make it correct.

Endothermic reactions .... energy overall from the

surroundings in the form of .... This is often shown

by a .... in ....

Q3 State whether bond **breaking** and bond **forming** are exothermic or endothermic reactions, and explain why in both cases.

Bond breaking ....

....

Bond forming ....

....

Q4 During the following reaction the reaction mixture's temperature **increases**.

A B + C ⟶ A C + B

a) Is the reaction exothermic or endothermic?

....

b) Which bond is stronger, A–B or A–C? Explain your answer.

....

Energy Transfer in Reactions

Q5   When **methane** burns in oxygen it forms carbon dioxide and water.
The bonds in the methane and oxygen molecules **break** and new bonds
are formed to make carbon dioxide and water molecules.

a)   Is energy taken in or given out when the bonds in the methane and oxygen molecules break?

....

b)   Is energy taken in or given out when the bonds in the carbon dioxide and water molecules form?

....

c)   Methane is a fuel commonly used in cooking and heating. Do you think that burning methane is
an exothermic or an endothermic process? Explain your answer.

....

....

d)   Which of the following statements about burning methane is true? Circle one letter.

A   **The energy involved in breaking bonds is greater than the energy involved in forming bonds.**

B   **The energy involved in breaking bonds is less than the energy involved in forming bonds.**

C   **The energy involved in breaking bonds is the same as the energy involved in forming bonds.**

Q6   Here are some practical uses of chemical reactions. Decide whether each reaction is
endothermic or **exothermic**. In the box, put **N** for endothermic and **X** for exothermic.

a)   A camping stove burns methylated spirit to heat a pan of beans.   ☐

b)   Special chemical cool packs are used by athletes to treat injuries.   ☐
They are placed on the skin and draw heat away from the injury.

c)   Self-heating cans of coffee contain chemicals in the base. When the   ☐
chemicals are combined they produce heat which warms the can.

d)   Cooking fried eggs and bacon for breakfast. ☐

This is different to part **a)** — think about what
happens to the eggs and bacon while they're cooking.

Energy Changes and Measuring Temperature

Q1 The **energy level diagrams** below represent the energy changes in five chemical reactions.

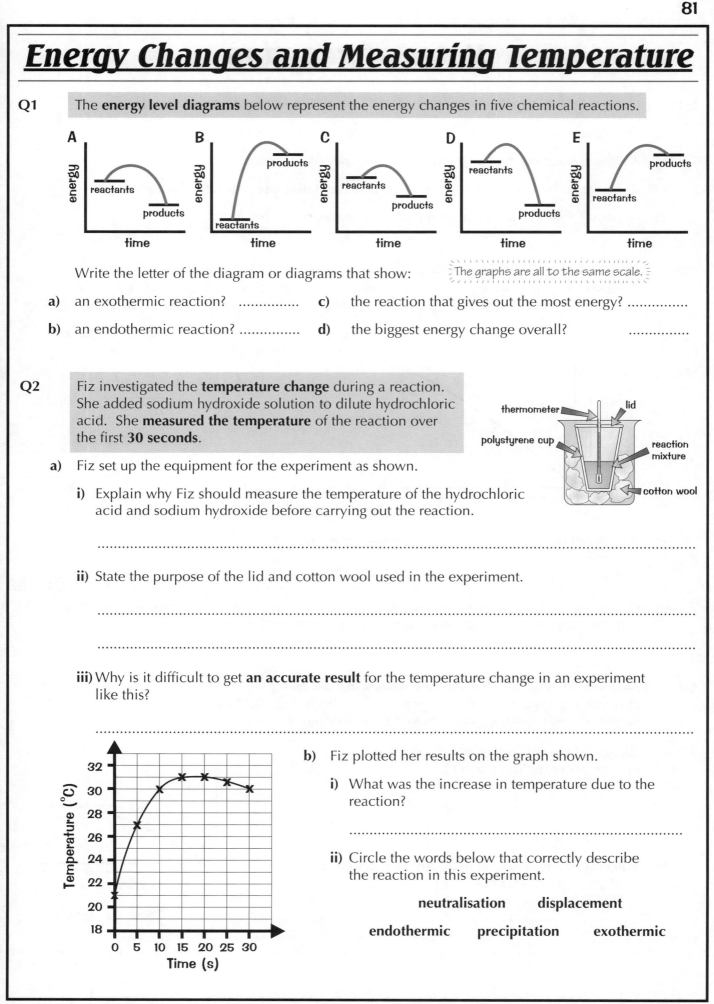

Write the letter of the diagram or diagrams that show:

The graphs are all to the same scale.

a) an exothermic reaction? ....

c) the reaction that gives out the most energy? ....

b) an endothermic reaction? ....

d) the biggest energy change overall? ....

Q2 Fiz investigated the **temperature change** during a reaction. She added sodium hydroxide solution to dilute hydrochloric acid. She **measured the temperature** of the reaction over the first **30 seconds**.

a) Fiz set up the equipment for the experiment as shown.

i) Explain why Fiz should measure the temperature of the hydrochloric acid and sodium hydroxide before carrying out the reaction.

....

ii) State the purpose of the lid and cotton wool used in the experiment.

....

....

iii) Why is it difficult to get **an accurate result** for the temperature change in an experiment like this?

....

b) Fiz plotted her results on the graph shown.

i) What was the increase in temperature due to the reaction?

....

ii) Circle the words below that correctly describe the reaction in this experiment.

> **neutralisation**   **displacement**
>
> **endothermic**   **precipitation**   **exothermic**

Rates of Reaction

Q1   Circle the correct words to complete the statements below about **rates of reaction**.

a)   The **higher** / **lower** the temperature, the faster the rate of a reaction.

b)   A **higher** / **lower** concentration will reduce the rate of a reaction.

c)   A smaller surface area of a solid reactant **increases** / **decreases** the rate of a reaction.

d)   A catalyst **does** / **does not** affect the rate of a reaction.

Q2   Marble chips with **different surface areas** were reacted with excess hydrochloric acid. The **same mass** of marble was used each time. The graph below shows the amount of **gas** evolved when using large marble chips (X), medium marble chips (Y) and small marble chips (Z).

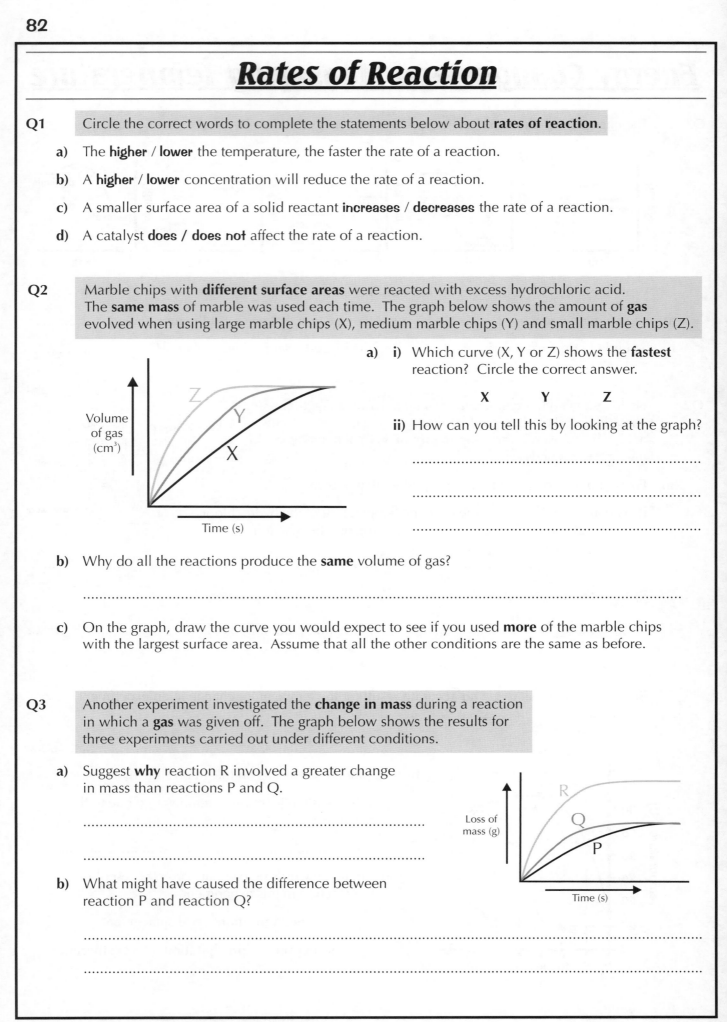

a) **i)** Which curve (X, Y or Z) shows the **fastest** reaction? Circle the correct answer.

          X   **Y**   **Z**

  ii) How can you tell this by looking at the graph?

....

....

....

b)   Why do all the reactions produce the **same** volume of gas?

....

c)   On the graph, draw the curve you would expect to see if you used **more** of the marble chips with the largest surface area. Assume that all the other conditions are the same as before.

Q3   Another experiment investigated the **change in mass** during a reaction in which a **gas** was given off. The graph below shows the results for three experiments carried out under different conditions.

a)   Suggest **why** reaction R involved a greater change in mass than reactions P and Q.

....

....

b)   What might have caused the difference between reaction P and reaction Q?

....

....

Rates of Reaction Experiments

Q1   Choose from the words below to complete the paragraph.

surface area	slower	react	decrease	faster	increase

When you crush up a large solid into powder, you .... its surface

area. This means it reacts .... Large lumps have a smaller

.... , so they .... more slowly.

Q2   Matilda conducted an experiment to investigate the effect of **surface area** on rate of reaction.
She added dilute hydrochloric acid to **large marble chips** and measured the volume of gas
produced at regular time intervals. She repeated the experiment using the same mass of
powdered marble. Below is a graph of her results.

a)   Which curve, A or B, was
obtained when **large pieces**
of marble were used?

....

b)   On the graph opposite, draw the
curve you would get if you used
the **same mass** of **medium** sized
marble pieces. Label it C.

Volume
of gas
(cm³)

A

B

Time (s)

c)   Balance the symbol equation for this reaction:

$$CaCO_3 + \quad HCl \rightarrow \quad CaCl_2 + \quad CO_2 + \quad H_2O$$

d)   Is there enough information given above for you to be sure whether this was a **fair test** or not?
Explain your answer.

....

....

....

e)   Matilda repeats the experiment using a greater mass of powdered marble.
How will this effect the volume of gas produced by the experiment?

....

Top Tips: The experiment on this page looks at the effect of surface area on the rate of a
reaction. But the same experiment can be used to measure any of the other factors that affect the rate.

Rates of Reaction Experiments

Q3 Sam did an experiment where marble chips were added to **highly concentrated** hydrochloric acid. He measured the **loss in mass** during the experiment. He did the experiment twice using the same conditions and then calculated averages for the results.

a) Why did Sam do the experiment **twice** and calculate averages for the results?

....

b) Sam did a second experiment in identical conditions but using a **lower concentration** of hydrochloric acid. The results of two runs are shown in the table below.

Time (s)	Run 1 — loss in mass (g)	Run 2 — loss in mass (g)	Average loss in mass (g)
5	1.1	0.9	
10	1.6	1.8	
15	2.7	2.3	
20	3.4	2.8	
25	3.6	3.4	
30	3.6	3.4	

i) Fill in the last column of the table by calculating the **average loss in mass** for the two experiments.

ii) The results of Sam's first experiment using highly concentrated of hydrochloric acid are shown below. Using the data you calculated in part **b) i)**, plot a line onto the graph showing the average loss in mass when Sam used a low concentration of hydrochloric acid.

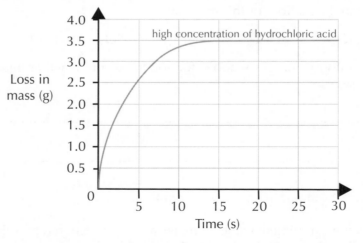

c) **Circle** the letter(s) to show the **valid conclusion(s)** you might draw from this graph.

    A   Rate of reaction depends on the temperature of the reactants.

    B   Increasing the concentration of the acid has no effect on the rate of reaction.

    C   Rate of reaction depends on the acid concentration.

    D   Rate of reaction depends on the mass of the marble chips.

Rates of Reaction Experiments and Catalysts

Q1 Yasmin investigates the effect of **temperature** on the rate of the reaction between sodium thiosulfate and hydrochloric acid. When they react, a precipitate is formed and the mixture becomes **cloudy**. She mixes the reactants together in a flask and times how long a cross placed under the flask takes to disappear.

Here are some results from her investigation:

Temperature (°C)	20	30	40	50	60
Time taken for cross to disappear (s)	201	177		112	82

a) As the temperature increases, does the reaction get **faster** or **slower**? ....

b) One of the values in the table is missing. Circle the most likely value for it from the list below.

145 s   192 s   115 s

Q2 The decomposition of hydrogen peroxide can be used to investigate the effect of a **catalyst** on the rate of reaction. A student compared three different catalysts to see which was the most effective (increased the rate of reaction the most). Below is a graph of his results.

a) Explain what a catalyst is and what it does.

....

....

b) i) The student finds that manganese (IV) oxide is the most effective catalyst for this reaction. Using the graph, decide which curve (R, S, or T) represents the reaction using manganese (IV) oxide. Circle the correct letter.

R   S   T

ii) Explain your answer.

....

....

Q3 **Catalytic converters** are used in car exhausts.

a) Describe what catalytic converters do.

....

....

b) Give two features of catalytic converters that make them well-suited to this role.

1. ....

2. ....

Collision Theory

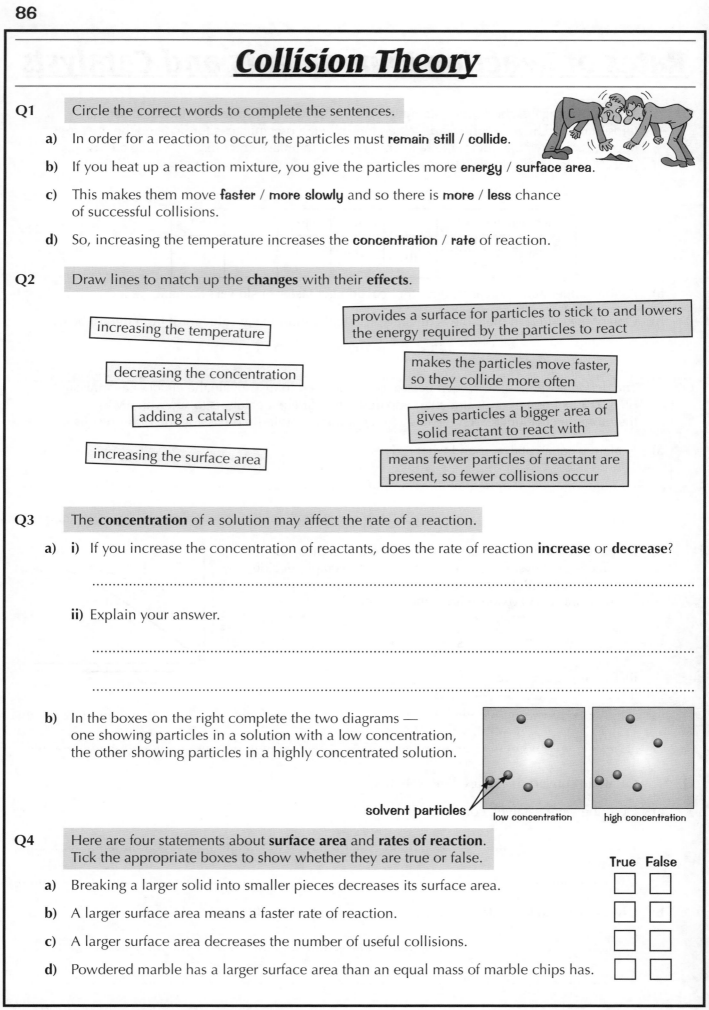

Q1 Circle the correct words to complete the sentences.

a) In order for a reaction to occur, the particles must **remain still** / **collide**.

b) If you heat up a reaction mixture, you give the particles more **energy** / **surface area**.

c) This makes them move **faster** / **more slowly** and so there is **more** / **less** chance of successful collisions.

d) So, increasing the temperature increases the **concentration** / **rate** of reaction.

Q2 Draw lines to match up the **changes** with their **effects**.

increasing the temperature

decreasing the concentration

adding a catalyst

increasing the surface area

provides a surface for particles to stick to and lowers the energy required by the particles to react

makes the particles move faster, so they collide more often

gives particles a bigger area of solid reactant to react with

means fewer particles of reactant are present, so fewer collisions occur

Q3 The **concentration** of a solution may affect the rate of a reaction.

a) i) If you increase the concentration of reactants, does the rate of reaction **increase** or **decrease**?

....

ii) Explain your answer.

....

....

b) In the boxes on the right complete the two diagrams —
one showing particles in a solution with a low concentration,
the other showing particles in a highly concentrated solution.

solvent particles

low concentration   high concentration

Q4 Here are four statements about **surface area** and **rates of reaction**.
Tick the appropriate boxes to show whether they are true or false.

True False

a) Breaking a larger solid into smaller pieces decreases its surface area. ☐ ☐

b) A larger surface area means a faster rate of reaction. ☐ ☐

c) A larger surface area decreases the number of useful collisions. ☐ ☐

d) Powdered marble has a larger surface area than an equal mass of marble chips has. ☐ ☐

Relative Formula Mass

Q1   What are the **relative atomic masses (A$_r$)** of the following:

a) magnesium ....

b) neon ....

c) oxygen ....

d) hydrogen ....

e) C ....

f) Cu ....

g) K ....

h) Ca ....

i) Cl ....

Q2   **Identify** the **elements** A, B and C.

Element A is ....

Element B is ....

Element C is ....

Element A has an A$_r$ of 4.
Element B has an A$_r$ 3 times that of element A.
Element C has an A$_r$ 4 times that of element A.

Q3 a)   Explain how the **relative formula mass** of a **compound** is calculated.

....

b)   What are the **relative formula masses (M$_r$)** of the following:

i) water (H_2O) ....

ii) calcium chloride ($CaCl_2$) ....

iii) potassium hydroxide (KOH) ....

iv) nitric acid (HNO_3) ....

v) sulfuric acid (H_2SO_4) ....

vi) ammonium nitrate (NH_4NO_3) ....

vii) aluminium sulfate ($Al_2(SO_4)_3$) ....

Q4   The equation below shows a reaction between an element, X, and water.
The total M$_r$ of the products is **114**. What is substance X?

$$2X + 2H_2O \rightarrow 2XOH + H_2$$

....

....

Top Tips: The periodic table really comes in useful here. There's no way you'll be able to answer these questions without one (unless you've memorised all the elements' relative atomic masses — and that would just be silly). And luckily for you, there's one in the front of this book.

Two Formula Mass Calculations

Q1 a) Write down the **formula** for calculating the **percentage mass** of an element in a compound.

b) Calculate the percentage mass of the following elements in ammonium nitrate, NH_4NO_3.

i) Nitrogen ....

ii) Hydrogen ....

iii) Oxygen ....

Q2 **Nitrogen monoxide**, NO, reacts with oxygen, O_2, to form **oxide R**.

a) Calculate the percentage mass of nitrogen in **nitrogen monoxide**.

....

b) A 100 g sample of oxide R contains **30.4 g** of **nitrogen** and **69.6 g** of **oxygen**.
Work out the empirical formula of oxide R.

....

....

....

Q3 **31.9 g** of **aluminium** reacts with **288.1 g** of **bromine** to form a compound.
Work out the empirical formula of the compound.

....

....

....

Q4 a) Calculate the percentage mass of **oxygen** in each of the following compounds.

| A | Fe_2O_3 | B | H_2O | C | $CaCO_3$ |

b) Which compound has the **greatest** percentage mass of oxygen? ....

Calculating Masses in Reactions

Q1 Anna burns **10 g** of **magnesium** in air to produce **magnesium oxide** (MgO).

a) Write out the **balanced equation** for this reaction.

....

b) Calculate the mass of **magnesium oxide** that's produced.

....

....

....

Q2 What mass of **sodium** is needed to make **2 g** of **sodium oxide**? $4Na + O_2 \rightarrow 2Na_2O$

....

....

....

Q3 **Aluminium** and **iron oxide** (Fe_2O_3) react together to produce **aluminium oxide** (Al_2O_3) and **iron**.

a) Write out the **balanced equation** for this reaction.

....

b) What **mass** of iron is produced from **20 g** of iron oxide?

....

....

....

Q4 When heated, **limestone** ($CaCO_3$) decomposes to form **calcium oxide** (CaO) and **carbon dioxide**.

How many **kilograms** of limestone are needed to make **100 kilograms** of **calcium oxide**?

The calculation is the same — just use 'kg' instead of 'g'.

....

....

....

....

Calculating Masses in Reactions

Q5 **Iron oxide** is reduced to **iron** inside a blast furnace using carbon. There are **three** stages involved.

Stage A	$C + O_2 \rightarrow CO_2$
Stage B	$CO_2 + C \rightarrow 2CO$
Stage C	$3CO + Fe_2O_3 \rightarrow 2Fe + 3CO_2$

a) If **10 g** of **carbon** are used in stage B, and all the carbon monoxide produced gets used in stage C, what **mass** of CO_2 is produced in **stage C**?

Work out the mass of CO at the end of stage B first.

....

....

....

....

b) Suggest what happens to the CO_2 produced in stage C.

Look at where CO_2 is used.

....

Q6 **Sodium sulfate** (Na_2SO_4) is made by reacting **sodium hydroxide** (NaOH) with **sulfuric acid** (H_2SO_4). **Water** is also produced.

a) Write out the **balanced equation** for this reaction.

....

b) What mass of **sodium hydroxide** is needed to make **75 g** of **sodium sulfate**?

....

....

....

....

c) What mass of **water** is formed when **50 g** of **sulfuric acid** reacts with sodium hydroxide?

....

....

....

....

Top Tips: Masses, equations, formulas — they can all seem a bit scary. But don't worry, practice makes perfect. And once you get the hang of them you'll wonder what all the fuss was about.

Percentage Yield

Q1   James wanted to produce **silver chloride** (AgCl). He added a carefully measured mass of silver nitrate to an excess of dilute hydrochloric acid. **1.2 g** of silver chloride was produced.

a)   Explain what is meant by the **yield** of a chemical reaction.

....

b)   **i)**   Write down the formula for calculating the **percentage yield** of a reaction.

....

ii)   James calculated that he should get 2.7 g of silver chloride. What was the **percentage yield**?

....

Q2   Aaliya and Natasha mixed together barium chloride ($BaCl_2$) and sodium sulfate (Na_2SO_4) in a beaker to produce barium sulfate. They **filtered** the solution to obtain the solid barium sulfate, and then transferred the barium sulfate to a clean piece of **filter paper** and left it to dry.

a)   Aaliya calculated that they should produce a yield of **15 g** of barium sulfate. However, after completing the experiment they found they had only obtained **6 g**.

Calculate the **percentage yield** for this reaction.

....

b)   Suggest two reasons why their actual yield was lower than their theoretical yield.

1. ....

....

2. ....

....

Q3   The reaction between magnesium and oxygen produces a white powder, **magnesium oxide**. Four samples of magnesium, each weighing 2 g, were burned and the oxide produced was weighed. The **expected** yield was **3.33 g**.

Sample	Mass of oxide (g)
A	3.00
B	3.18
C	3.05
D	3.15

a)   What is the percentage yield for each sample?

....

....

....

b)   Which of the following are possible reasons why the yield was not 100%? Circle their letters.

A   Some of the oxide was lost before it was weighed   **B**   Too much magnesium was burned

C   Not all of the magnesium was burned   **D**   The reaction was too fast

Percentage Yield

Q4 Complete the table of results showing the **percentage yields** from different experiments.

You can use the space below for working out.

Actual yield	Theoretical yield	Percentage yield
3.4 g	4.0 g	a)
6.4 g	7.2 g	b)
3.6 g	c)	80%
d)	6.5 g	90%

Q5 Fill in the gaps to complete the passage below using the words from the box.

waste	expensive	yield	harmful	speed	environment	commercially

Chemical reactions can produce lots of unwanted .... products.

These can be .... and may pose a threat to the ....

It can be .... to dispose of these products safely. Chemists look to

find reactions that give a high percentage .... , produce

.... useful products and take place at a suitable ....

Q6 Limestone consists of **calcium carbonate**. If calcium carbonate is heated it leaves solid **calcium oxide**. When **100 tonnes** of limestone were heated, **42 tonnes** of calcium oxide were produced.

a) Write the equation for this reaction. ....

Use a periodic table to help you with this question.

b) What was the theoretical yield?

....

....

c) Using your answer from part **b)**, calculate the percentage yield.

....

d) Why are you unlikely ever to get a 100% yield from this process?

....

....

Mixed Questions — C2b Topics 4, 5 & 6

Q1 The results of a reaction between **calcium carbonate** and **hydrochloric acid** are shown on the graph.

a) The products of this reaction are calcium chloride (which forms a colourless solution), water and carbon dioxide. Suggest how the rate of this reaction could be measured.

....

....

b) Which part of the curve shows the fastest rate of reaction — A, B or C? ....

c) Explain what happens to the reaction at point C.

....

d) i) At 35 °C, the reaction followed the curve shown on the graph. Draw two other complete curves on the same diagram to show how the rate of reaction might change at 25 °C and 45 °C.

ii) Explain why raising the temperature affects the rate of reaction.

....

....

e) Give three factors other than temperature that affect the rate of reaction.

....

Q2 **Iodine** vapour reacts with **hydrogen** to form hydrogen iodide.
The reaction is **endothermic** and the mixture turns from purple to colourless.

I I + H H → H I H I

a) Which old bonds are broken?

....

b) Which new bonds are made?

....

c) Which of the processes is endothermic — breaking bonds or forming new ones?

....

d) Do you think that the temperature of the reaction vessel will rise or fall during this reaction? Explain your answer.

....

....

Mixed Questions — C2b Topics 4, 5 & 6

Q3 In many reactions, a **catalyst** can be used to increase the **reaction rate**.

a) Explain how a catalyst works.

....

....

b) Which form would be better as a catalyst, a stick or a powder? Explain your answer.

....

....

Q4 Orwell found that **1.4 g** of **silicon** reacted with **7.1 g** of **chlorine** to produce the reactive liquid silicon chloride.

a) Work out the **empirical formula** of the silicon chloride.

....

....

b) Calculate the **percentage mass** of chlorine in silicon chloride.

....

....

c) Write down the balanced chemical equation for the reaction.

....

d) Orwell predicted he would obtain 8.5 g of silicon chloride, however he only obtained 6.5 g. Calculate the percentage yield for this reaction.

....

Q5 **Aqueous chlorine**, Cl_2, was added to **potassium bromide solution**, KBr. Aqueous chlorine is pale green and potassium bromide is colourless.

a) Complete and **balance** the following chemical equation:

$$Cl_2 + \text{............. } KBr \rightarrow \text{..................... } + \text{.....................}$$

b) What would you observe when the two reactants are mixed?

....

c) Suggest why bromine solution will **not** react with aqueous potassium chloride.

....

C2b Topic 6 — Quantitative Chemistry

Analysing Substances

Q1   Use the words to complete the passage.

much	only	quantitative	sample	qualitative

> The first stage in any analysis is to choose the most suitable analytical method.
>
> A .... method can be used if you .... want
>
> to find out what substances are present in a ...., but if you
>
> want to find out how .... of each substance is present then a
>
> .... analysis is necessary.

Q2   Give **two situations** where analytical techniques are used.

    1. ....

    2. ....

Q3   Maria was asked to identify the **solute** present in a sample of water. It was known to be a single ionic compound.

> Step 1 — Maria took 5 cm³ of the water and added a small quantity of sodium hydroxide solution. A **white precipitate** was formed that dissolved when more of the alkali was added. This told Maria that the **aluminium ion** was present.
>
> Step 2 — Maria took a further 25 cm³ of water and added some dilute hydrochloric acid followed by an excess of barium chloride solution. A **white precipitate** was formed showing Maria that the **sulfate ion** was present.

  a) Explain why the test for an ion must be unique.

      ....

  b) Circle the correct answer for each of the following questions.

      i) What sort of analysis is carried out in Step 1 of the procedure? **qualitative / quantitative**

      ii) What sort of analysis is carried out in Step 2 of the procedure? **qualitative / quantitative**

  c) What must be the identity of the mystery solute? ....

Top Tips: Chemical analysis is vital — chemists often need to know what's in a substance. Make sure you know what qualitative and quantitative analyses are, and be ready to explain how you'd identify ionic compounds — remember you have to test for both the positive and the negative ion.

Testing for Ions

Q1   Robert adds a solution of **sodium hydroxide** to a solution of **calcium chloride**. The symbol for the calcium ion is Ca^{2+}.

a)   What would Robert observe?

....

b)   Write the balanced symbol equation for the reaction, including state symbols.

....

c)   Write the balanced **ionic equation** for this reaction, including state symbols.

....

Q2   Cilla adds a few drops of **NaOH** solution to solutions of different **metal compounds**.

a)   Complete her table of results.

Metal Cation	Colour of Precipitate
Fe^{2+}	
	blue
Fe^{3+}	
Al^{3+}	

b)   Complete the balanced ionic equation for the reaction of iron(II) ions with hydroxide ions.

Fe^{2+}(........) + ... OH^-(aq) → .... (s)

c)   Write a balanced **ionic** equation for the reaction of **iron(III) ions** with hydroxide ions.

....

Don't forget state symbols.

d)   Cilla adds a few drops of sodium hydroxide solution to **aluminium sulfate solution**. She continues adding sodium hydroxide to excess. What would she observe at each stage?

....

....

Q3   Deirdre wants to find out if a soluble compound contains **chloride**, **bromide** or **iodide** ions. Explain how she could do this.

....

....

....

Testing for Ions

Q4   Select compounds from the box to match the following statements.

FeSO$_4$ contains the Fe^{2+} ion and FeCl$_3$ contains the Fe^{3+} ion.

KCl	LiCl	FeSO$_4$	NH$_4$Cl	FeCl$_3$	Al$_2$(SO$_4$)$_3$
NaCl	CuSO$_4$	CaCl$_2$	MgCl$_2$	BaCl$_2$	

a)   This compound forms a blue precipitate with sodium hydroxide solution. ....

b)   This compound forms a white precipitate with sodium hydroxide that dissolves if excess sodium hydroxide is added. ....

c)   This compound forms a green precipitate with sodium hydroxide solution. ....

d)   This compound forms a brown precipitate with sodium hydroxide solution. ....

e)   This compound reacts with sodium hydroxide to release a pungent gas. ....

f)   This compound reacts with sodium hydroxide to form a white precipitate, and it also gives a brick-red flame in a flame test. ....

Q5   Claire was given a solid sample of a mixture of two ionic compounds. She was told that they were thought to be **ammonium chloride** and **calcium chloride**.

a)   Describe, in detail, how she would test for the presence of the two **positive ions**.

....

....

....

b)   What would she **observe** at each stage?

....

....

....

c)   Write **ionic equations** for the reactions that identify the positive ions.

....

....

Top Tips: Right, this stuff needs to be learnt properly. Otherwise you'll be stuck in your exam staring at a question about the colour that some random solution goes when you add something you've never heard of before to it, and all you'll know is that ammonia smells of cat wee.

Measuring Amounts

Q1 a) **Complete** the following sentence.

> One mole of atoms or molecules of any substance will have a .... in grams
>
> equal to the .... for that substance.

b) Write down the **formula** for calculating the **mass** of a substance from the number of moles.

....

c) What is the **mass** of each of the following?

i) 1 mole of copper ....

ii) 3 moles of chlorine **gas** ....

iii) 2 moles of nitric acid (HNO_3) ....

iv) 2.5 moles of NaOH ....

v) 0.5 moles of calcium carbonate ($CaCO_3$) ....

Q2 a) Write down the formula for calculating the **number of moles in a given mass**.

....

b) How many **moles** are there in each of the following?

i) 20 g of calcium ....

ii) 112 g of sulfur ....

iii) 200 g of copper oxide (CuO) ....

iv) 110 g of carbon dioxide (CO_2) ....

c) Calculate the **mass** of each of the following.

i) 2 moles of sodium ....

ii) 1.25 moles of aluminium ....

iii) 0.75 moles of magnesium oxide (MgO) ....

iv) 0.025 moles of lead chloride ($PbCl_2$) ....

Top Tips: Everyone hates calculations but I'm afraid this page is full of them. Make sure you know which formula to use before you begin. Then do them all — it's the only way you'll get better.

Solutions and Concentrations

Q1 Complete the table by calculating the **mass-concentration** for each of these solutions.

MASS (g)	VOLUME	MASS–CONCENTRATION (g/dm³)
2	4 dm³	a)
4.6	2 dm³	b)
0.8	500 cm³	c)
0.2	100 cm³	d)

Q2 Concentration can be measured in **moles/dm³** or **g/dm³**.

How many moles?

a) Convert the following solution concentrations from moles/dm³ to g/dm³.

   i) 2 mol/dm³ sodium hydroxide, NaOH.

   ....

   ....

   ii) 0.1 mol/dm³ glucose, $C_6H_{12}O_6$.

   ....

   ....

b) A solution of HCl has a mass-concentration of 3.8 g/dm³. Calculate its mole-concentration.

....

....

Q3 Susan wants to work out the concentration of a solution of sodium chloride. She puts 10 g of the solution in a pre-weighed, clean, dry evaporating basin and heats the basin until all the water appears to have evaporated.

a) What would Susan do next? Explain why she would do this.

....

....

....

b) After doing this, how can she calculate the mass of sodium chloride that was dissolved?

....

....

Hard Water

Q1   Tick the correct boxes to show whether the statements are **true** or **false**.

		True	False
a)	Water can be softened by removing chloride and carbonate ions from the water.	☐	☐
b)	Adding sodium chloride is one way of removing hardness from water.	☐	☐
c)	When soap is used with hard water, it forms a lather easily.	☐	☐
d)	You can remove the hardness from water by adding sodium carbonate.	☐	☐

Q2   An **ion exchange resin** can be used to remove the hardness from water.

a) Circle the ions below that are responsible for causing hard water.

Ca^{2+} OH^- Ca^{3+} Mg^{2+} Na^+ Cl^- H^+

b) Explain how hard water becomes soft when it is passed through an **ion exchange resin**.

....

....

....

c) Does this method work for permanent hardness, temporary hardness, or both?

....

Q3   In an experiment to investigate the **causes** of **hardness** in water, soap solution was added to different solutions. Five drops were added at a time until a sustainable lather was formed.

Distilled water has been purified to remove metal ions.

Solution	Drops of soap solution needed to produce a lather	Observations
distilled water	5	no scum
magnesium sulfate solution	35	scum formed
calcium chloride solution	30	scum formed
sodium chloride solution	5	no scum

a) Why must all the solutions be prepared from distilled water rather than tap water?

....

b) **i)** Which compounds caused hardness in the water?

....

ii) Explain how you know.

....

Titrations

Q1 Circle the answer which best completes each of these sentences.

a) During acid-base titrations...

...methyl orange is always a suitable indicator.   ...the alkali must always go in the burette.

...the tap is opened fully near the end of the titration.   ...the flask is swirled regularly.

b) An acid-base titration is an example of a...

...precipitation reaction.   ...displacement reaction.

...neutralisation reaction.   ...reduction reaction.

c) Acid-base titrations are used to find...

...the rate of a reaction.   ...the concentration of an acid or base.

...the concentration of a salt.   ...the volume of a solution.

Q2 Circle the correct words below to complete the passage about how to do a titration.

> Using a pipette and **measuring cylinder / pipette filler**, add some alkali to a conical flask, along with two or three drops of **indicator / litmus** solution. Using a **burette / pipette filler**, add acid to the alkali a bit at a time and give it a regular swirl. There's a colour change when all the alkali has been **dissolved / neutralised**. Record the **volume / temperature** of the **acid / alkali** used.

Q3 A **titration** procedure was used to compare the some fizzy drinks. The base used for the titration was sodium hydroxide solution.

a) Write down the **ionic equation** for this titration reaction.

....

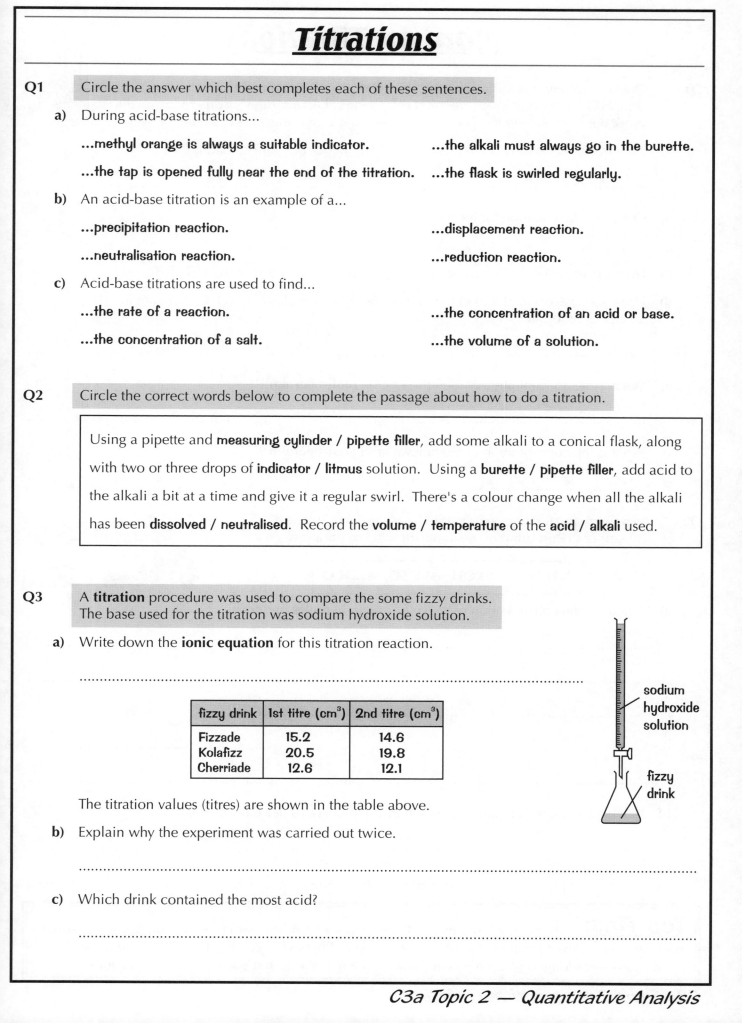

sodium hydroxide solution

fizzy drink

fizzy drink	1st titre (cm^3)	2nd titre (cm^3)
Fizzade	15.2	14.6
Kolafizz	20.5	19.8
Cherriade	12.6	12.1

The titration values (titres) are shown in the table above.

b) Explain why the experiment was carried out twice.

....

c) Which drink contained the most acid?

....

More on Titrations

Q1 The concentration of some limewater, **Ca(OH)$_2$**, was determined by titration with hydrochloric acid, **HCl**. **50 cm³** of limewater required **20 cm³** of **0.1 mol/dm³** hydrochloric acid to neutralise it. Work out the concentration of the limewater in **g/dm³** using the steps outlined below.

a) How many moles of HCl are present in 20 cm³ of 0.1 mol/dm³ solution?

....

b) Complete the equation for the reaction.

.... + ... → CaCl$_2$ + ...

c) From the equation, ... mole(s) of HCl reacts with .... mole(s) of Ca(OH)$_2$.

d) Use your answers to **a)** and **c)** to work out how many moles of Ca(OH)$_2$ there are in 50 cm³ of limewater.

....

e) What is the concentration of the limewater in **moles per dm³**?

....

f) What is the concentration of the limewater in **grams per dm³**?

....

Q2 In a titration, **10 cm³** of sulfuric acid was used to neutralise **30 cm³** of **0.1 mol/dm³** potassium hydroxide solution.

$$H_2SO_4 + 2KOH \rightarrow K_2SO_4 + 2H_2O$$

a) Calculate the concentration of the sulfuric acid in **moles per dm³**.

....

....

....

....

....

b) Calculate the concentration of the sulfuric acid in **grams per dm³**.

....

....

Top Tips: Aargh, not more calculations... As if Chemistry wasn't tricky enough without some maths getting involved too (but at least it's not as bad as Physics). Actually, these aren't the worst calculations — as long as you remember to tackle them in stages and you know your equations.

C3a Topic 2 — Quantitative Analysis

Preparing Soluble Salts

Q1   **Nickel sulfate** (a soluble salt) was made by adding **insoluble nickel carbonate** to **sulfuric acid** until no further reaction occurred.

a)   State how you would know when the reaction is complete.

....

Once the reaction was complete, the excess nickel carbonate was separated from the nickel sulfate solution using the apparatus shown.

b)   Label the diagram which shows the separation process.

....

....

....

c)   What is this method of separation called?

....

d)   Describe how you could produce a solid sample of nickel sulfate from nickel sulfate solution.

....

....

e)   Potassium hydroxide is a **soluble salt**. It reacts with sulfuric acid to form **potassium sulfate**.

i)   Explain **why** the method used to make nickel sulfate needs to be modified for this reaction.

....

....

....

ii) Explain **how** you would modify the method.

....

....

....

....

Electrolysis of Molten Substances

Q1 Explain why the **electrolyte** needs to be either a **solution** or **molten** for electrolysis to work.

....

....

....

Q2 **Molten sodium chloride** can be split up by electrolysis.

a) Tick the boxes to show whether the following statements are **true** or **false**.

                                                                                                   True   **False**

    i) The chloride ions are oxidised.

    ii) Chloride ions are attracted to the negative cathode.

    iii) The sodium ions are reduced.

    iv) Sodium ions are attracted to the positive anode.

    v) Electrolysis always involves either reduction or oxidation, never both.

b) State two uses for the sodium made by electrolysis.

    1. ....

    2. ....

Q3 **Molten lead bromide** ($PbBr_2$) is electrolysed using inert electrodes.

a) i) Give the **anion** in this reaction. ....

    ii) Write the half-equation for the reaction at the **anode**. ....

b) i) Give the **cation** in this reaction. ....

    ii) Write the half-equation for the reaction at the **cathode**. ....

Q4 **Complete** and **balance** the following electrode reactions.
For each one, tick the correct box to show whether it is **oxidation** or **reduction**.

                                                         Oxidation **Reduction**

a) $Na^+ + ... \rightarrow ....$

b) $Cu^{2+} + ...e^- \rightarrow ....$

c) $........OH^- \rightarrow ....H_2O + O_2 + ...e^-$

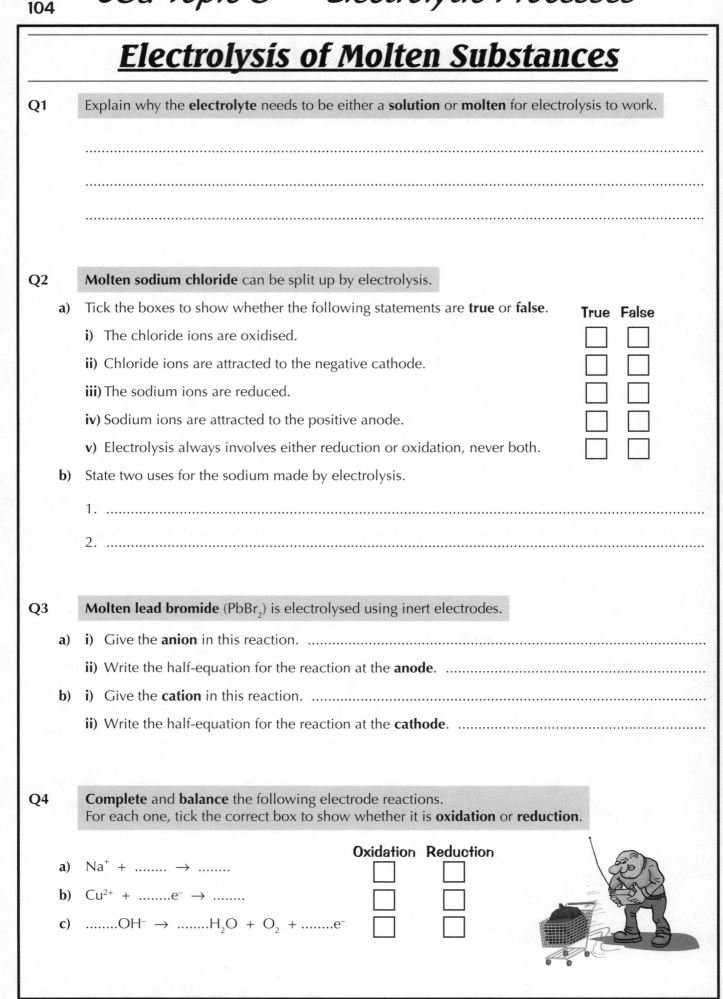

Electrolysis of Solutions

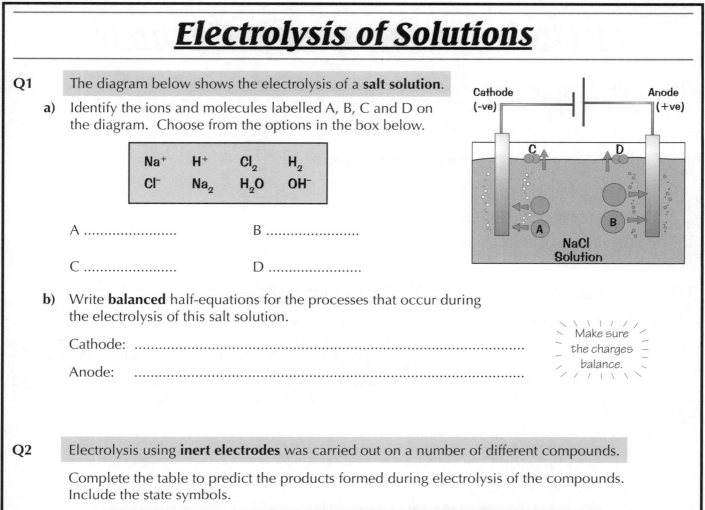

Q1 The diagram below shows the electrolysis of a **salt solution**.

a) Identify the ions and molecules labelled A, B, C and D on the diagram. Choose from the options in the box below.

Na^+	H^+	Cl_2	H_2
Cl^-	Na_2	H_2O	OH^-

A ....   B ....

C ....   D ....

b) Write **balanced** half-equations for the processes that occur during the electrolysis of this salt solution.

Cathode: ....

Anode: ....

Make sure the charges balance.

Q2 Electrolysis using **inert electrodes** was carried out on a number of different compounds.

Complete the table to predict the products formed during electrolysis of the compounds. Include the state symbols.

Compound	Product formed at the:	
	cathode	**anode**
copper chloride solution		
copper sulfate solution		
sodium sulfate solution		

Q3 Explain why the electrolysis of **molten** ionic salts is different from salts in **solution**.

....

....

....

....

....

Electrolysis Using Copper Electrodes

Q1   Why would it **not** be a good idea to carry out the electrolysis of **copper** in an electrolyte that contained **zinc** ions instead of copper ions? Tick the correct box.

The zinc ions will not conduct an electrical current. ☐

The copper produced will have zinc impurities in it. ☐

A poisonous gas would be produced. ☐

The zinc and copper ions will react with each other. ☐

The zinc ions will coat the anode. ☐

Q2   The diagram below shows the purification of **copper** by electrolysis.

a) Identify the labels A to D on the diagram. Choose from the options in the box.

copper ions   copper atoms   impure copper electrode
copper sulfate solution   pure copper electrode   batteries

A ....

B ....

C ....

D ....

b) Write down the half equations for the reactions at:

i) the anode ....

ii) the cathode ....

c) When copper is purified by electrolysis, **impure sludge** simply falls to the bottom. It does **not** move to the cathode. Suggest why this happens.

Think about why substances move between the electrodes.

....

....

d) The table below shows the mass of the two electrodes before and after the experiment.

	Electrode A (mass in g)	Electrode B (mass in g)
Before	122.6	19.7
After	34.0	113.9

Which electrode is the anode? Explain your answer.

....

....

Electroplating

Q1   Fill in the gaps in the passage below using some of the words from the box.

gold	appearance	carbon	unreactive	strong	malleability	corroding

There are a number of reasons why metals are electroplated. Jewellery can be

electroplated with .... to improve the ....

of the metal. Other metals can be electroplated to stop them ....

Metals used for this reason must be ....

Q2   Lily is carrying out an experiment to electroplate **zinc** onto a **copper rod**.

  a) Which material should Lily use for:

    i) the anode? ....

    ii) the cathode? ....

  b) **i)** Circle the compound in the list below that Lily should use as the electrolyte.

            copper sulfate   hydrochloric acid   zinc sulfate

    ii) Explain your choice.

      ....

      ....

Q3   Electroplating could be used to put a
thin coat of **silver** onto a **nickel** fork.

  a) Complete the diagram by labelling
the **cathode** and **anode**.

  b) What ion must the electrolyte contain?

      ....

  c) Give the half equation for the reaction at:

    i) the anode ....

    ii) the cathode ....

**pure
silver
strip**

Top Tips: Electroplating is an important use for electrolysis in the real world. The trick with
an electroplating question is to make sure you're clear about which metal is being to plated onto which.
The electrolyte will have to contain the ions of the plating metal or the whole thing won't work.

Mixed Questions — C3a Topics 1, 2 & 3

Q1 'Test The Water' are a company who measure the purity of tap water.
They analysed a 238 cm³ sample of water and find that it contains **0.1 g of iron**.

a) What is the **mass-concentration** of iron in the water?

....

....

b) Was the analysis carried out **qualitative** or **quantitative**?

....

Q2 Sam is taking part in a chemistry competition where she needs to be able to identify various **ions**.

a) Sam has a flowchart to help her identify **halide ions** present in a water sample.
Complete the gaps in her flowchart.

```
                                                        white
                                                     precipitate ──── ...... ions
water      add .................    add .................
sample     .................        .................    ................. ──── Br⁻ ions
                                                        precipitate

                                                     ................. ──── I⁻ ions
                                                      precipitate
```

b) What type of analysis would this be? ....

c) Sam has another flowchart for identifying **positive ions**.
Fill in the gaps.

```
                                              ................. ──── Ca²⁺ ions
                                               precipitate
Solution of      add .................
mystery          .................            ................. ──── Cu²⁺ ions
compound                                       precipitate

                                                  green       ──── ........ ions
                                               precipitate
```

d) Sam knows that if she adds sodium hydroxide solution to a solution of aluminium ions, there will be a white precipitate which will then redissolve in excess sodium hydroxide to form a colourless solution. Write the ionic equations including state symbols for these two reactions.

....

....

Mixed Questions — C3a Topics 1, 2 & 3

Q3 Magnesium reacts with nitric acid, HNO_3, to form **magnesium nitrate**, $Mg(NO_3)_2$, and hydrogen.

a) Work out the relative formula mass of magnesium nitrate.

....

b) When 0.12 g of magnesium reacted with excess acid, 0.74 g of magnesium nitrate was formed.

i) Calculate the number of moles of magnesium that reacted and the number of moles of magnesium nitrate produced.

....

....

ii) If 0.025 moles of nitric acid was used, what mass of nitric acid was this?

....

Q4 Hyde tested samples of water from three different **rivers** using the following method.

> 8 cm³ of river water was placed in a test tube.
> 1 cm³ of soap solution was added and the tube was shaken.
> More soap was added until a lasting lather was produced.
> The amount of soap solution needed was recorded.
> The experiment was repeated with boiled water from the river.

The results of the experiment are shown in the table.

a) Which river contained the softest water? ....

b) Which river contained the hardest water? ....

c) Why was less soap needed to form a lasting lather after the water from river A was boiled?

RIVER	AMOUNT OF SOAP NEEDED (cm³)	
	PLAIN WATER	BOILED WATER
A	7	5
B	2	2
C	4	4

....

....

....

d) The hardness in rivers B and C could not be removed by boiling.

i) State the name given to this type of hardness.

....

ii) Suggest one way of removing the hardness from rivers B and C.

....

Mixed Questions — C3a Topics 1, 2 & 3

Q5   An **electric current** is passed through **molten lead bromide**, as shown in the diagram.

a)   What is this process called?

....

b)   Why does the lead bromide have to be molten?

....

....

c)   Lead bromide, $PbBr_2$, is composed of Pb^{2+} and Br^- ions.

   i)   State which ion moves toward each electrode during this process.

   Electrode A   ....   Electrode B   ....

   ii)   Balance the following half equations for the reactions.

   $$Pb^{2+} \; + \quad e^- \rightarrow \quad Pb \qquad\qquad\qquad Br^- \rightarrow \quad Br_2 \; + \quad e^-$$

Q6   Dean carried out a titration to calculate the concentration of a sample of HCl.

a)   Dean set up his equipment as shown. Label the three pieces of equipment marked X, Y and Z.

   Z ....

   X ....

   Y ....

b)   20 cm³ of 0.5 mol/dm³ sodium hydroxide solution was used to neutralise 25 cm³ of hydrochloric acid. What is the **concentration** of the acid, in:

   i)   moles per dm³? ....

   ....

   ....

   ii)   grams per dm³? ....

   ....

   ....

C3a Topic 3 — Electrolytic Processes

Calculating Volumes

Q1 a) What is the **volume** of **one mole** of any gas at room temperature and pressure? Circle your answer.

$24\ dm^3$ $\qquad$ $12\ dm^3$ $\qquad$ $2.4\ dm^3$ $\qquad$ $36\ dm^3$

b) What is the name given to this volume? Circle your answer.

mass volume $\qquad$ room volume $\qquad$ Avogadro's volume $\qquad$ molar volume

c) What volume is occupied by the following gases at room temperature and pressure?

i) 0.5 moles of hydrogen chloride. ....

ii) 6.25 moles of ammonia. ....

d) How many moles are there in the following gases at room temperature and pressure?

i) 240 cm³ of hydrogen. ....

ii) 8 dm³ of chlorine. ....

Q2 The **limewater test** for carbon dioxide involves the reaction between carbon dioxide and calcium hydroxide, which is shown in the following equation:

$$CO_{2\ (g)} + Ca(OH)_{2\ (aq)} \rightarrow CaCO_{3\ (s)} + H_2O_{\ (l)}$$

RTP stands for 'room temperature and pressure'.

A solution of limewater containing 0.37 g of calcium hydroxide reacts with carbon dioxide at RTP.

a) What mass of **carbon dioxide** is needed to react completely with the limewater?

....

....

b) What **volume** does this amount of carbon dioxide occupy at RTP?

....

Q3 **Sulfur dioxide** (SO_2) is a gas produced when sulfur burns in oxygen.

a) Write down the **chemical equation** for this reaction.

....

b) Calculate the relative molecular mass (M_r) of **SO_2**.

....

c) Calculate the **volume** of sulfur dioxide produced when **144 g** of sulfur burns in oxygen.

....

....

....

....

Reversible Reactions

Q1   Use words from the list below to complete the following sentences about **reversible reactions**.

| escape | reactants | closed | products | react | balance |

a) In a reversible reaction, the .... of the reaction can themselves

.... to give the original ....

b) At equilibrium, the amounts of reactants and products reach a ....

c) To reach equilibrium the reaction must happen in a .... system

where products and reactants can't ....

Q2   Which of these statements about reversible reactions are **true** and which are **false**?

		True	False
a)	The position of an equilibrium depends on the reaction conditions.	☐	☐
b)	Upon reaching a dynamic equilibrium, the reactions stop taking place.	☐	☐
c)	You can move the position of equilibrium to get more product.	☐	☐
d)	At equilibrium there will always be equal quantities of products and reactants.	☐	☐

Q3   Look at this diagram of a **reversible reaction**.

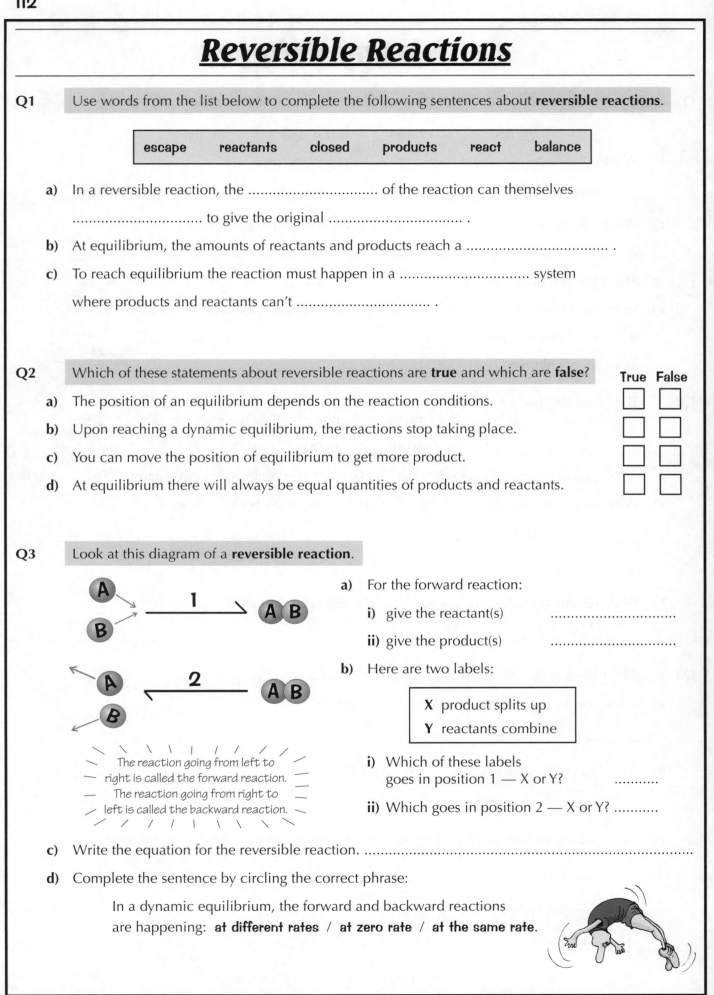

a) For the forward reaction:

i) give the reactant(s)   ....

ii) give the product(s)   ....

b) Here are two labels:

> **X** product splits up
>
> **Y** reactants combine

The reaction going from left to right is called the forward reaction. The reaction going from right to left is called the backward reaction.

i) Which of these labels goes in position 1 — X or Y?   ....

ii) Which goes in position 2 — X or Y? ....

c) Write the equation for the reversible reaction. ....

d) Complete the sentence by circling the correct phrase:

In a dynamic equilibrium, the forward and backward reactions
are happening: **at different rates** / **at zero rate** / **at the same rate**.

Reversible Reactions

Q4 Substances A and B react to produce substances C and D in a **reversible reaction**.

$$2A(g) + B(g) \rightleftharpoons 2C(g) + D(g)$$

a) The forward reaction is **exothermic**. Does the backward reaction give out or take in heat? Explain your answer.

....

....

b) If the temperature is raised, will the equilibrium position move to the left or to the right?

....

c) Explain why changing the **temperature** of a reversible reaction always affects the position of the equilibrium.

....

....

d) Explain the effect of changing the **pressure** on the position of equilibrium in this reaction.

....

....

Q5 Look at the equation showing another **reversible reaction**.

$$2SO_2(g) + O_2(g) \rightleftharpoons 2SO_3(g)$$

a) i) Explain which reaction, forward or backward, is accompanied by a **decrease** in volume.

....

....

ii) How will increasing the pressure affect the position of equilibrium in this reaction?

....

....

b) What does adding a catalyst to a reversible reaction do? Circle the letter next to your answer.

    A It moves the equilibrium position towards the products.

    B It makes the reaction reach equilibrium more quickly.

    C It moves the equilibrium position towards the reactants.

    D It causes a decrease in pressure.

c) What happens to the amount of product at equilibrium when you use a catalyst?

....

The Haber Process

Q1   The Haber process is used to make **ammonia**. The equation for the reaction is:

$$N_2(g) + 3H_2(g) \rightleftharpoons 2NH_3(g)$$

a)   Name the reactants in the forward reaction. ....

b)   Which side of the equation has more molecules? ....

c)   How should the pressure be changed in order to produce more ammonia? Explain your answer.

....

....

Q2   The **industrial conditions** for the Haber process are shown below.

Pressure: 200 atmospheres   Temperature: 450 °C

a)   Suggest why a pressure greater than 200 atmospheres is not used.

....

b)   In the Haber process reaction, the **forward** reaction is **exothermic**.

   i)   What effect will raising the temperature have on the **amount** of ammonia formed?

   ....

   ii) Explain why a high temperature is used industrially.

   ....

   ....

Q3   Stuart is a farmer. He uses **fertilisers** manufactured from ammonia to help his plants grow.

a)   What name is given to fertilisers manufactured from ammonia?

....

b)   Some of the fertiliser used by Stuart is washed into a lake next to his land.
     Explain the possible **environmental consequences** of this.

....

....

....

....

Homologous Series

Q1 Fill in the gaps in the passage below using the words from the box.

physical	elements	chemical	general	boiling points	molecular

A homologous series is a group of compounds with the same ....

formula. This means that the compounds contain the same ....

and have similar .... structures. The compounds have similar

.... properties but show gradual variation in their

.... properties. For example, the ....

of compounds in a homologous series increase as their size increases.

Q2 Below are the names of four different **hydrocarbons** from the same homologous series.

a) Write the molecular formula and draw the structural formula
for the following hydrocarbons. One has been done for you.

Name	Molecular formula	Structural formula
methane	....	
ethane	C_2H_6	H—C—C—H (with H above and below each C)
propane	....	
butane	....	

b) What name is given to this family of hydrocarbons?

....

Homologous Series

Q3 The **structural formulas** of alcohols can be used to identify them and determine their **properties**.

a) Circle any of the following molecular and structural formulas that represent alcohols.

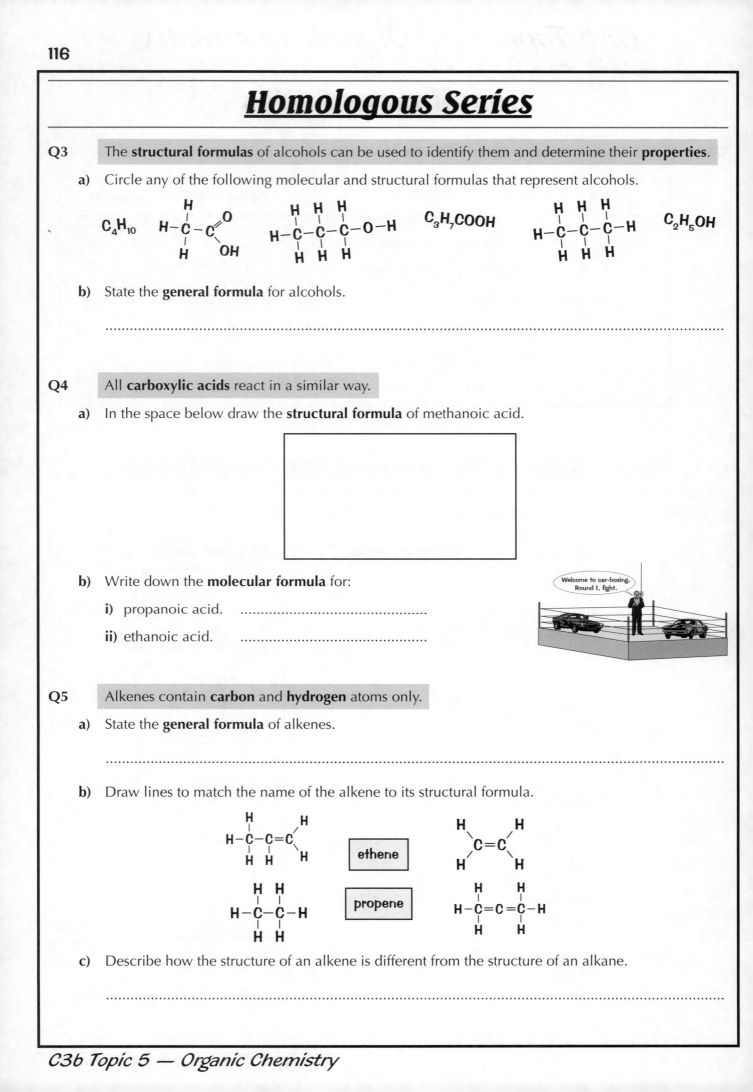

C_4H_{10}

C_3H_7COOH

C_2H_5OH

b) State the **general formula** for alcohols.

....

Q4 All **carboxylic acids** react in a similar way.

a) In the space below draw the **structural formula** of methanoic acid.

b) Write down the **molecular formula** for:

i) propanoic acid. ....

ii) ethanoic acid. ....

Welcome to car-boxing.
Round 1, fight.

Q5 Alkenes contain **carbon** and **hydrogen** atoms only.

a) State the **general formula** of alkenes.

....

b) Draw lines to match the name of the alkene to its structural formula.

ethene

propene

c) Describe how the structure of an alkene is different from the structure of an alkane.

....

Production of Ethanol

Q1   Ethanol is produced using **fermentation**.

a)   Complete the following sentences by choosing the correct words from the list below.

concentration	carbohydrates	ethene	anaerobic
enzyme	aerobic	temperature	ester

i) Fermentation is used to turn .... into ethanol.

ii) The reaction happens due to an .... found in yeast.

iii) The .... needs to be carefully controlled during the reaction.

iv) The process of fermentation is carried out under .... conditions.

b)   Which of the following is the correct equation for the production
of ethanol from glucose? Circle A, B, C or D.

$$A \qquad C_6H_{12}O_6 \rightarrow 2C_2H_5OH + 2CO_2$$

$$B \qquad C_6H_{12}O_6 \rightarrow 2C_2H_5OH + 2O_2$$

$$C \qquad C_6H_{12}O_6 \rightarrow 2C_2H_5OH + H_2O$$

$$D \qquad C_6H_{12}O_6 \rightarrow 2C_2H_5OH + 2CH_4$$

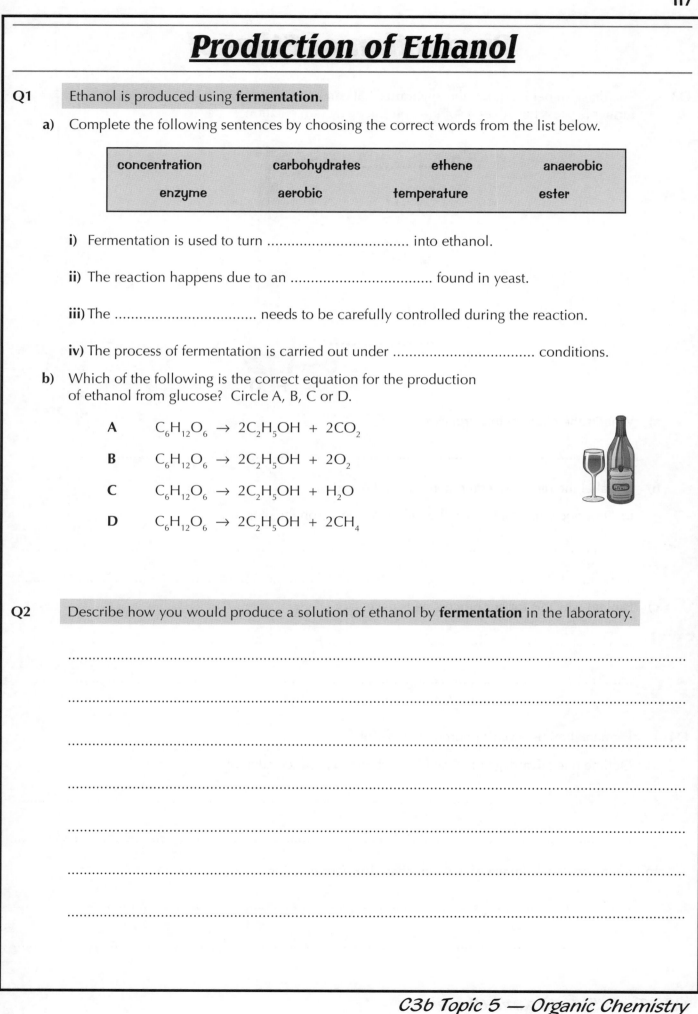

Q2   Describe how you would produce a solution of ethanol by **fermentation** in the laboratory.

....

....

....

....

....

....

....

Production of Ethanol

Q3 The diagram below shows the **apparatus** that can be used to further process the ethanol solution produced by fermentation.

A ....

D

B ....

....

C —

HEAT

a) What is the name of this process?

....

b) **i)** Label the pieces of equipment marked A and B.

ii) Describe what happens at the following places on the diagram.

C ....

D ....

c) Explain why this further processing is necessary.

....

....

Q4 Fermentation uses yeast to produce ethanol.

a) Outline one **advantage** of using fermentation to produce ethanol.

....

....

b) Give one **disadvantage** of making ethanol by fermentation.

....

....

Production and Issues of Ethanol

Q1 Fermentation is not used for **large-scale production** of high quality **ethanol**.

a) Which of the following is the correct word equation for the reaction used to produce ethanol? Circle the correct answer.

ethane + steam → ethanol

ethanoic acid + steam → ethanol

ethyl ethanoate + steam → ethanol

ethene + steam → ethanol

b) Give one **advantage** of using this method to produce ethanol.

....

Q2 Rachel is giving a presentation in class about the impacts of excessive alcohol drinking on society.

Rachel says: "Getting drunk can lead to vandalism and violence."

Suggest three other costs to **society** of excessive alcohol drinking.

1. ....

2. ....

3. ....

Q3 Excessive **alcohol** intake can have **damaging effects** on the human body.

Describe the damaging effects that alcohol may have on the body.

....

....

....

....

....

....

Ethene and Ethanoic Acid

Q1 Ethanol can be used to make **ethene**.

a) Write a symbol equation for the conversion of ethanol into ethene.

....

b) Circle the correct word below to show the name of this process.

          dehydration   polymerisation   oxidation   cracking

Q2 Wine that has been left open to the air for several days often tastes like **vinegar**.

a) Explain why wine that has been left open tastes like vinegar.

....

....

b) State one use for vinegar.

....

Q3 **Ethanoic acid** displays the reactions of a typical acid.

a) **i)** Write the word equation for the reaction between ethanoic acid and calcium.

....

ii) Write the symbol equation for this reaction.

....

b) Fill in the gaps to complete the symbol equation below for the reaction between ethanoic acid and the base potassium hydroxide.

.... + KOH $\longrightarrow$ .... + ...

c) Circle the products below that are formed in the reaction between ethanoic acid and sodium carbonate.

| hydrogen | sodium ethanoate | water |

| sodium chloride | carbon dioxide | oxygen |

d) Describe the effect of ethanoic acid on litmus paper.

....

Esters

Q1   Recycled **polyesters** are used in the manufacture of clothing.

a)   Circle the clothing material below that can be made using recycled polyester.

wool   cotton   fleece   denim

b)   Name one other use for polyesters, apart from in clothing.

....

Q2   Hermione works for a **perfume manufacturer**. She frequently uses **esters**, since they are commonly used in perfume production.

a)   Give one property of esters that make them suited for use in perfumes.

....

b)   Part of Hermione's job involves producing an ester called ethyl ethanoate.

Which of the following represents the correct reaction for the production of ethyl ethanoate? Circle the correct answer.

ethanol + water → ethyl ethanoate + carbon dioxide

ethanol + ethane → ethyl ethanoate + water

magnesium oxide + ethanoic acid → ethyl ethanoate + water

ethanol + ethanoic acid → ethyl ethanoate + water

c)   In the space below, draw the structural formula of **ethyl ethanoate**.

d)   Other than perfumes, give one use of esters in the chemical industry.

Esther — also runs
for parliament

....

Top Tips: Esters really are great, but they don't only occur in industry. The smells and flavours of most fruits are caused by esters. Make sure you've got the basics under your hat, like the general word equation for the formation of an ester and all the different uses of esters.

Uses of Esters

Q1   Soaps and detergents are made from **fatty acids**.

a)   Fill in the gaps to complete the sentences below.

i)   Fats and oils are types of ....

ii)   Soaps are made by .... oils and fats

in a concentrated .... solution.

b)   The diagram below shows a labelled **soap anion**.

hydrophilic head ◀————〜〜〜〜————▶ hydrophobic tail

Which section of the molecule is attracted to:

i)   water molecules?   ....

ii)   grease and oil?   ....

c)   Describe how soap molecules lift oily stains out of fabric.

....

....

....

Q2   Unsaturated oils can be converted into solid saturated fats.

a)   Explain what is meant by the terms **saturated** and **unsaturated**.

....

....

b)   i)   What is the name of the process used to convert liquid oils into saturated fats?

....

ii)   Describe what happens to the unsaturated oils during this process.

....

....

....

c)   Name one product in the food industry that is made using this process.

....

Mixed Questions — C3b Topics 4 & 5

Q1 **Ethanol** can be produced by **fermentation** or by the **hydration** of **ethene**.

a) Write the word equation for the fermentation of glucose.

....

b) Describe an **advantage** that the hydration of ethene has over fermentation.

....

c) At the moment, the production of ethanol by hydration of ethene is a **cheap** process. Explain why it will soon become more expensive.

....

....

....

Q2 **Avogadro's Law** is used to calculate the volume of a gas.

a) State Avogadro's law.

....

....

b) The chemical equation for the formation of hydrogen peroxide is shown below.

$$H_{2(g)} + O_{2(g)} \rightarrow H_2O_{2(g)}$$

i) Find the volume of hydrogen peroxide produced when **3.8 g** of oxygen reacts with hydrogen.

$$\text{Volume of gas (dm}^3) = \frac{\text{Mass of gas (g)}}{M_r \text{ of gas}} \times 24$$

....

....

....

....

ii) What volume of hydrogen is needed to produce this volume of hydrogen peroxide?

....

c) Calculate the volume of **6.2 moles** of H_2O_2 at room temperature and pressure.

....

....

Mixed Questions — C3b Topics 4 & 5

Q3   If exposed to the air, **ethanol** in wine is converted to **ethanoic acid**.

a) i) State the word equation for the formation of ethanoic acid from ethanol.

....

ii) What type of reaction is this? Circle the word from the list below.

| oxidation | neutralisation | reduction | dehydration |

b) Write down the balanced symbol equation for the reaction between ethanoic acid and sodium carbonate.

The chemical formula for sodium carbonate is Na_2CO_3.

....

Q4   The Paper Street Soap Company make soaps by reacting **esters** with **sodium hydroxide**.

a) i) Esters are an example of a **homologous series**.
Describe what is meant by the term 'homologous series'.

....

....

ii) Describe how the boiling points of esters change as the size of the molecules **increases**.

....

b) i) State the word equation for the formation of an ester from the reaction between ethanoic acid and ethanol.

....

ii) Draw the structural formula equation for the reaction between ethanoic acid and ethanol.

c) Describe how an ester and sodium hydroxide are used to produce soap.

....

....

....